Words and Worlds Anthology Vol. 3

we are so much more

ISBN: 978-1-915314-05-5

Get in touch: Hello@MustardStoriesArts.co.uk

Typeset by Simon Jamie at Fingermouse Books.

Special Thanks

Newcastle University
Charlie Wilkinson
Blue Sky Trust
Anxious Minds
Coping with Cancer
Recovery College Collective
Martin Type Photography

Portrait photography by Andy Martin
martintype.co.uk

Cover design by Isabella Clark

Illustration by Tamsin Rees

Foreword

The Words & Worlds project was originally commissioned by Newcastle City Council in response to COVID-19 and led by artists Natasha Haws and Elijah Young 2020-2021. The intention of this residency was to help people from different community groups share their stories. After the success of the first project, we have continued to work with communities to provide a platform for their voices and have now established a community interest company under the name Mustard Stories Arts.

This is the third iteration of the Words and Worlds project which has been commissioned by the Faculty of Medical Sciences at Newcastle University. We worked from May to October 2022 with over 40 participants who all live with a long-term health condition which has led to the creation of this third volume.

This anthology explores the theme of Health & Wellbeing. For this project we partnered with different community groups:

Blue Sky Trust - An organisation that supports those living with HIV.

ReCoCo - Recovery College Collective run support groups and activities for those in recovery from mental illness, substance misuse, trauma or distress.

Anxious Minds - A community hub in Wallsend that supports those living with different mental health conditions.

Coping with Cancer - An organisation that supports those living with or affected by cancer.

We also worked remotely via email with the members of the general public who wanted to share their experience of their long-term health condition. This included people living with autism, parkinsons, chronic pain, OCD, depression, anxiety, mobility issues, spina bifida and also have experience as a carer.

One of the hopes of this anthology is to inform and influence the future of health research and to act as an example to researchers how they can engage the general public in their research in more meaningful and impactful ways. If you are reading this anthology as a researcher, it's important to note not every piece explicitly states the long term conditions people are living with. If you would like further information, an extended version of this anthology has been created as a research resource. To find out more, contact fms.engagemnet@ncl.ac.uk

Some of the work in this anthology is deliberately unedited to celebrate the uniqueness of every individual voice. Some pieces are credited with pseudonyms/anonymously to allow the participants to write freely and honestly. Some are scribed by us to allow those who struggle with literacy or the English language to still take part. We believe each and every one of the participants are now writers in their own right and as Mustard Stories Arts, we wanted to help tell the stories of these people who are so much more than the health condition they live with.

"We are so much more than a diagnosis."
- David Oliver

Contents

Content warning:
Some pieces include themes of grief, self-harm, suicidal thoughts and mental health.

The Gendered Experience   *139*

The NHS   *151*

A Place   *165*

Milestones

Sharing the milestones of life and how we got to this point.

"Everything that happens to you, is how you are created."

Beginning

by Liz Parkinson

I was born on a Saturday afternoon on the 3rd of March 1956 in the city of Belfast, my mother's home.

When I was about a year old we left Belfast and went to live in my father's home in the North East of England. But of course I don't remember any of this.

My first memory is of sitting on the edge of a bed with my legs dangling down. This was my first memory, my first realisation of existence. I would have been about two and a half years of age. It's like that was my beginning. I have no memory of what went before. In that moment, I was connected. I knew I existed. I knew I was alive. Of that time I have a dull memory of a baby sister who I had no interest in, didn't feel any connection with. She was just there.

My mother was a small thin woman with long dark hair with a wonky fringe. If anyone had cast an eye they would not have thought her pretty, plain or ugly, just a small, thin woman with long dark hair and a wonky fringe, but she did have nice blue eyes.

My father I barely remember from that time, he would just appear then be gone. We lived in a caravan on a farmers field.

I was quite young when I was first let out to play.

I was a feral child. I ran. I screamed. I laughed. I fought. I cried.

All this I did with other kids who lived in caravans on a farmers field.

We were feral, unwashed. We had no bounds, no rules, just space the ground beneath our feet and high endless skies. But a ta ta went a tommy gun. Bang bang went a cowboy gun. You're dead, play dead and I did. Laying with my back on the ground and my eyes tight shut.

I could feel the raging thud of life beneath me and I wanted to laugh out loud.

I turned and lay face down in the ground and stuck my tongue out and licked the ground and the earth was bitter sweet. She tasted of blood and honey.

I stood up and wiped the dirt from my mouth and laughed and danced.

You're dead, play dead, but I wasn't, I was alive.

18TH June 1959

by Isabel Marafao

I was born on the 18th of June 1959, far away from here in east Africa, Mozambique.

When war exploded, for the independence of Moz from Portugal, my parents sent me in 1974 to South Africa and then to Portugal where I finished my studies and started as a tourism officer for 35 years and then came to the UK Newcastle in 2016.

My oldest memory was when I was three years old: my mum took me to the barber and he cut my hair. I remember the colour of a giant chair, the colour was beige. The Barber put wood above the arms of the chair and started to make streets, roads on my head?! I was so surprised.

This happens because my mum got bored with me because I borrowed her hair scissors and by myself I cut my hair. When mum saw me like that she quickly ran me to the barber.

1987 When I was working at my tourism office, I married a man from Spain, Nayard. He died in 1991, I became a widow with a virus that he passed to me. He died of AIDS and didn't tell me anything about it.

Life is hard but I am here with 50 years of diabetes and 30 years of being HIV positive, well supported with love around.

Liz Gregson

Different experience

by Liz Gregson

My eye condition due Oculocutaneous Albinism is complex; the effects include nystagmus, being unable to see small details and sensitivity to sunlight. I have had to wear glasses since I was a toddler; the lenses used to be very thick, until thinner lenses were developed. I often wear sunglasses and a hat to avoid being dazzled. Even wearing glasses I have difficulty seeing, have to be careful and look closely. For reading I need a clear, well defined font with a good contrast.

I have difficulty seeing fine details, so when I'm outdoors I often don't see wildlife and it's hard to distinguish different species without guidance, which can be frustrating.

"I missed it" is my mantra.

As a child I never understood my eye condition or what "albino" meant. No one explained it to me, other than I needed to wear glasses all the time. At school I couldn't read the blackboard. There was no assisted technology then, so I had to manage by listening or sometimes going to the front near the teacher, so I could copy diagrams. It was embarrassing, but I had to get used to it. At University it was helpful when I was given hard copies of information. Team sport was a trial to be avoided, as it was hard to see the ball, but I enjoyed athletics.

I accepted I have never been able to drive, but it has limited my choices where I could live and work. Aspects of public transport are inaccessible; bus numbers are hard to read until the bus is close, meaning I sometimes miss the bus I need. Reading bus timetables and train departure boards is a challenge, particularly digital displays, often situated high above eye level. I had to quickly learn to ask others to read them.

As an adult it took me a long time to get detailed information about albinism and my resulting eye condition to understand it. I have noticed people have difficulty understanding the impact this has and the barriers I experience in my life. For years I found this hard, but I became more confident during my career when involved with disability groups. I now recognise barriers are created by society, rather than my personal inability and challenge these when appropriate and ask for help when I need it.

Technology has become helpful in many aspects of everyday life, including specialised lighting and equipment, but it also marginalises me in other ways.

Websites and apps are often designed to appear stylish, but in the pursuit of aesthetics they sometimes lack clear font and good contrast, so become inaccessible. Subtitles are hard to read, particularly when displayed on a patterned background, so I am unable to follow foreign films and documentaries when speech in foreign languages is not dubbed.

My eye condition means my life experiences and choices have been different to fully sighted people; I acknowledge this and manage this as well as possible to lead a full, active life.

Born 1994, Ghana

by AA

I was brought up with my grandma, it was lovely until I lost my grandma and my whole life turned upside down. Since then I have not been like before.

I remember going to the farm with my grandma. She would sing for me, she would tell me stories.

We had a cocoa farm, we had a lake close by, I would have my bath in the lake. It was such a lovely place, a very calm place. No disturbance, very beautiful. You can see mountains all over, big trees and birds.

When I was 13 my grandma died. She died on top of me. I stopped going to school. I thought she was sleeping. I tried to wake her up but she didn't. A man said she is sleeping. They put her in a room and covered her in leaves.

"What are they doing to her? She isn't sleeping."

I went to her room, I thought I heard her, but when I woke up she's sleeping. Because I am close to her, her spirit can't go to the land of the dead. She was everything to me. I trusted her my whole life.

But I was sick. I came to Carlisle. They diagnosed me at the hospital. I went into a coma.

I saw my grandma and she told me to go back. I saw her beside my consultant. I wanted to tell her my grandma is here. I hear the voices, they put a mask on me.

Since my grandma died, I can't trust my family. The way people behave they wash things I touch. Life is not smooth the way I thought it would be.

I always remember my grandma saying "Everything that happens to you, is how you are created. Once it is part of you, it is part of you. It is your destiny."

HIV and me

by Mark Barham

When I was 25 my life went a bit downhill.

It was a Monday morning and I was a chef in a hotel in Henley upon Thames. I had just put lasagne in the oven when my boss came into the kitchen and told me my uncle was on the phone. When I got to the phone and he told me that they had found my sister's body the day before, I just fell to the ground. My boss's daughter knew something was wrong and called for help. My sister had been murdered in the Philipines while travelling the world.

I left work and went to a friend's house and they took me to where all the family were. That was the only time that I ever hugged my dad, we were not a huggy type family.

This was the only time that I have ever been sad.

I left work as I couldn't cope and moved to Brighton then London. I was 25 years old.

I was in a relationship with a chap however I had a one night stand and the following morning he told me he had Aids, I'm not a violent person and just left. Back then you had to wait 3 months for results to come back from a HIV test. I went home to my partner and explained, not only had I had an affair but possibly contracted HIV.

I went to oldchurch hospital gum clinic as they were called back then and they informed me that I was HIV positive. My partner was negative so that was great.

I started on 27 tablets a day, yeah I rattled lol.

This started my journey of visiting HIV support groups around the country. Fast forward a couple of years and I had a good job in a London Arts centre , I informed my boss that I had HIV and a few weeks later I was fired. I took him to a tribunal for unfair dismissal and settled out of court. This took a lot out of me and I felt upset and confused on how people could treat you like that.

I moved to Stevenage with my new work but got into debt with credit cards and such, this was when I was declared bankrupt for the first time. It would have been around 2005.

Even though I had been declared bankrupt, 6 years later I decided to open up my own cafe in a business centre in Southampton. I have been in and out of chef work since I left school.

I had gone to Eastleigh college to get some chef qualifications and all was going well until I noticed certain businesses were not coming to the cafe. I had recently been shortlisted for a business award which made the papers, however they disclosed my HIV status.

Businesses had stopped coming because they thought they could catch HIV from the sausages. After that the damage was done and I was in debt again to about 18000 pounds. Bring on bankruptcy number 2.

I remained strong throughout this period of my life due to my great friends that I had around me. I was volunteering with several charities at this point and also late 2011 I was asked to become Patron of Thames Valley Positive Support. I was so happy again and have been to some amazing places, including a garden party at Buckingham Palace.

Care

Taking care; of ourselves, others and the community.

"I give myself the gift of time."

Let your watchword be take care

by Tony Moore

I look after myself. I care for myself. I don't look after anyone else. I don't care for anyone else. Or do I?

Daisy was wandering around the building that I live in the other day. She was lost. I asked if she was okay. She asked if I could take her home. I did, no problem. I took her to her apartment. She asked if I could come in with her. I did. She said we could sit for a while. She said she did not know what this place was, but could I take her home.

She had set the table in her own home that morning, she recalled. She had set it for her husband. "'Clive will be wondering where I am! I haven't seen him since this morning" she voiced. Clive had died almost a decade ago.

I saw Daisy wandering again a few days later, she had a pottery cat in her hand.

"She has been following me about all day. I know where her mother is – I am taking her to her mother".

Make sure you have got your keys then Daisy, and do not go too far. I kept an eye on her from my window. Daisy was wandering around the building again today. She seemed upset. She was chatting to Eva and her daughter Mandy. She said 'oh good, here is Tony, he will know what to do.' I thought she might be concerned that her jumper was on inside out and back to front. This wasn't bothering her at all. She had more sinister things on her mind. She was concerned because there was a baby in her bed wrapped in her blankets. I went to check in her apartment. No baby. A lot of her clothes were laid out on the bed. 'They must have taken the baby' she proclaimed.

'Yes, they must have', I added, they will be looking after her. Don't you worry about it Daisy.

I don't challenge what Daisy says. I go along with her. I listen, I hear, I sit with her. I reassure her. I care.

Care

by AA

If I feel sad I don't have anyone to talk to.
I go to the forest.
I do my own planting.
If I see my sugar cane growing, I am more happy.
Anything I've achieved makes me more happier.

It's hard to talk to people.
To trust somebody is very hard for me.
I make myself more busy with my children.
I have been through a lot. I don't trust anybody.
Being alone in the house, talking to no one, watching the TV.
It makes me think, why is life being unfair to me? My family, my sickness.

If I see plants growing, I feel more happier.
Every plant doesn't care whether it's going to rain or not.

How do I care for myself?

by DK

I've never been good at caring for myself, I often fall into self-destructive behaviour, which often undoes the things I've done to improve my wellbeing. I use strong painkillers as part of living with a lifelong condition, however it becomes too easy to fall into patterns of abuse when I go through difficult periods. Not caring about myself has had a knock on effect, it's cost me friends, girlfriends, education and physical and mental health and left others to pick up the pieces.

I couldn't take care of myself because I didn't care about myself, I used to let my chronic pain dominate my life and it broke me. I abused my insides with oxycodone and my outsides with razor blades. Then my best friend took his own life and seeing that affect our friends and his family, I knew I had to take better care of myself, not for me but for others, I couldn't put people through that.

While there have been relapses, I'm taking much better care of myself, I'm almost back down to a healthy weight and I weaned myself off of the Oxycodone over the course of the pandemic, and went onto a sensible dose of morphine instead. I cut out opiates all together for 4 months but I disappointingly had to go back on them because my pain control just wasn't great and that caused me for the first time in 11 years to self harm again. At least it was pain and not my need to get high, so I haven't beaten myself up too much about it.

While I had 4 months of thinking clearly, or as clearly as my unhinged mind will allow, I started doing things to improve my mental health, groups at the doctors, the Recovery College, mindfulness, all things I would have dismissed as "a load of crap" even just a year ago and it really has helped me help myself.

I still struggle with my mind but I'm in a better place to deal with it now.

I take care of myself

by Gift

I take care of myself.

First I should look after myself. I should find something to relax my mind.

When I'm at a wrong with myself, I love football. So when football comes on the screen of the tele, I enjoy it. The women of England won the trophee, I was happy for that.

No one can care for you, they are there to help you but you should look after yourself. Some people are there to help you to be good. If you've got a problem go to someone, ask them, they'll help. If you got ill, you got to the doctors. But the most important thing is to take care of yourself. If you don't take care of yourself no one can take care of you.

People must look at themselves like the condition we have. Sometimes I know my condition is bad but I go for a smoke, I go for a drink. I drink too much which is not good for my health. No one stopped me but I should think to myself I should not do that. I can do this. I can do this.

People are there to help but you should help yourself. You are the priority.

David Black

Who cares?

by David Black

Caring as part of a family unit is always preferable to caring on your own. I've learned this idea the hard way. Being at home with mum, dad and I meant that we had three people around, if one of us disappeared we would have at least one other person left. I was an only child; this was great and fine when all three of us were at home. Thinking back, the summers were long and hot, and the winters were snowy and cold. It felt like we would all be here forever. As if it would never end.

It was after mum, and dad had returned from holiday abroad that we were first visited by a tragedy. They both loved holidays abroad, the hotter the better, but this time dad had suffered from a sudden bout of illness and had been struggling to get his breath in the heat. It was 2003 and after some investigation dad was diagnosed, he had cancer in or around the windpipe. This previously fit and healthy gentleman in his 70's was devastated by the news. I can't even begin to describe how mum and I were feeling.

My abiding memory of this time was dad going through the house with mum and tidying up everything from photographs to his creative writing. Getting the records of his life in order. When we lost him, it was rapid, and it left us with a feeling of no control, of a disease that ran wild and with free rein. The cancer acted with unrestricted liberty of action or decision.

Then we were left, mum and I, the two of us, ourselves alone. We had to just get on with it as we were alive, and life demanded we continue. All change, mum went through the house, and the bathroom, kitchen and bedrooms were modernized. I continued to work hard and not much happened for a decade. No one could have believed as we went about our daily lives with infinite complacency that unsympathetic tragedy would return to bother us again. But then it was the start of some more substantive change for us again.

It started with two unrelated things, a change for me at work and mum starting to get a bit forgetful. Mum's memory issues were relating to silly things, leaving the iron on clothing a bit too long, hiding stuff around the house and then forgetting about it. It brought dementia into our lives; it crept like a sycophantic work colleague at a meeting. Things slowed down and it felt like we were in the eye of the storm.

Unlike dad, who had returned from holiday feeling unwell, received a diagnosis and a time scale for what time was left, refused treatment to the horror of clinicians, and died at home shortly after, mums' dementia was a slow and torturous journey. What I'm seeing with mum is a drawn out, slow retreat of the body's functions as the brain's damage works its way through to every speck of mum's soul. Ultimately, being told she needed round the clock twenty-four hour care away from the family home, was the last straw for me.

My lived experience is of a discombobulating, disjointed, designed for the few not the many social care regime. Mum is being cared for, she still shows flickers of care for me, and is in a caring environment, but the many costs of dementia make it like a bereavement every day. The stuffed suits in boardrooms full of the nodding heads of privileged individuals making a career out of the human misery of health and social care is a million miles away from the dedicated cleaners and caregivers with a real vocation. Good people and bad people, life and death, the rich and the poor. We fight on whilst those in charge like the self-actualized sovereign individuals they seek to become fiddle while the system burns. For the few self-preservations what's really going on today.

Couples

by Mary O'Sullivan-Fawcett

It's hard to be a wife, husband or partner when you're carer
The lines start to blur
Hurt and resentment hang in the air
And with just one word or look you're back in your corners

Or with just one word or look you're enfolded in each other arms
And that is the best place to be
But it can be so hard to return to
If you've spent the day doing the worst tasks
    and both of you hating having to do them

So bring in the paid carers
Doing the jobs no one wants to, sometimes with minimum training
For very little pay and often no thanks from the recipients
I can tell you honestly though, there are some real diamonds out there

They come into your home, their workplace
You have to give guidelines, rules of the house
As a carer of a loved one, you have to step back
Let the person receiving care get to know the new carer

If it isn't working, for whatever reason
Don't give up, there are agencies, other carers, funding
Ask for help and, before too long
There will be trust, it's a slow, sometimes difficult, process

But before too long
You'll all smile when you greet each other
There will be hard times but you'll have each other's back
Most importantly though
You'll be a loving couple once again,
    as some of the daily chores have been picked

Caring for my mother

by Liz Parkinson

I remember my mother when she was young. She was always in an endless rage. She always had her fists clenched tight, ready for a fight. My mother was consumed by grief and rage, it had wrapped itself around her and held her tight and fast, I remember that she was not loved.

She was thought of as something less and treated as something less. I hated that. I wanted to protect her, to save her, to love her.But I could not. I started looking after my mother when I was 9. I was quite young. I did not realise I was caring for her. I was always trying to fix things, make everything alright but I could not. My mother was lost. She was lost for years and years.

Lost in a putrid cruel storm, a tidal wave of violence, hate and pain. Focus finally came when she was an older woman. Exhausted, age and illness quelled the storm and buried it deep, laid it to rest where it had always belonged. The rage had gone and my mother was calm.

I remember caring for my mother when she was old. Lighting her cigarette, giving her an ashtray, making her cups of tea while she watched TV. She was happy enough then, she was calm, the rage had gone. I was the 'good' and 'dutiful' daughter.

I never left, I stayed, I had no choice. Now that she is gone and what of me.

Well time is what it is and so it moves on. But sometimes I remember my mother and I realise that I could never have soothed her grief.

I could never have calmed her rage.
I could never have been more than what she had lost.
I could never ever have loved her more than what had been taken.

I hope now that this is true that her soul is free. That her soul is light and joyous and she is happy.

Seen, heard and understood

Who listened? Who understood? Who made an impact?

*"I see me for who I am and for all I feel.
No one else quite does, not completely. Not for real."*

Someone who made you feel seen

by David Oliver

I cast my mind back. Sat before me is a mountain of paperwork from the DWP. We were going to tribunal... Again. Endless questions about my life with this thing. This thing that I know I have. But how do I communicate how this thing feels, an unstoppable freight train. In the past they have ignored and twisted words. They ignored and they were determined to make things as difficult as they could be. This was not my first time at the rodeo. I'd been here several times before. They don't seem to like people with disabilities that much. The stress, and the isolation is thumping. Everything had once again turned to chaos as my life was once again uprooted.

That's when I discovered them. Disability North. Advocacy Heroes. They were going to walk me through the entire process, fill out forms and enforce a no-nonsense approach with the DWP. They ensured me that the systemic rejections were a common place and that I wasn't alone. For the first time since the beginning of this circle of hell I had the backing of someone who was just as sick of the system as me. They had been through this process thousands of times before. In an endless circle, they brought a scenic railway to help ease the endless stress and confusion. And I love scenic railway.

It wasn't going to take away the impending doom of having to go through it all over again, but at least I had backup. At least I had someone who had seen the circle happen many times before me. At least I didn't feel so alone. Whatever the DWP continued to throw at me, it wasn't quite so bad. Having someone to immediately step in and assume battle position made me feel like a force to be reckoned with.

The day of the tribunal came. It was intense. I'd been here before but somehow it was different. There was a vast support network of people fighting my corner. Ready to take action and call the DWP out for their long and tiresome history of mistakes, Systemic failings, and incompetency. Some of which was downright baffling to say the least.

The DWP could no longer find a reason as to why it had gotten this far. Six months to hear those words was an overpowering sense of frustration, joy and yet anger. Gradually things got sorted, settled and back to some semblance of normality. And I will be forever grateful to all those who have helped thus far in this circle of doom and gloom and fighting for what I'm entitled to. Of course, it never stopped the circle. To this day it continues. Like an inevitable moth against a lightbulb. But for that moment and that round someone was there. It continues to be a tricky existence, funnily enough having a disability isn't cheap. To this day I talk about my experiences. In the hopes to highlight the ridiculousness of the DWP and let others know they are not alone.

Brave

by AD

Louise.
When I first got diagnosed,
supported, discussed, not alone.
I still have life, normal life.
Different organisations;
Blue Sky Trust, the RVI
help me by medication.
So kind and caring, supporting, checking on me.
When it comes to living in UK, hasn't been easy.
House to house, city to city.
Sometimes I don't know anybody.
Stockton is lonely
but things will work out.

Vulnerability Literacy

by Pip McDonald

Monologuing in a wave of radical honesty
Tectonic shifts and raw inevitability
Opening up new quantum chapters of a new book
I did not know that this book existed

I shared some ideas and feelings with a friend
It was quite scary
but felt a real shift afterwards
that opened a new level of friendship for us both
a safe space to share how we feel

Oh and I was able to write some new poems

Invisible

by Barry Wilkinson

I was born at home. I popped out on the kitchen floor. Not totally unexpectedly but a little too quickly for my Mam. I had serious issues, I was born with Spina Bifida, a congenital defect where the spine does not develop properly and remains open allowing nerves to come through externally. This and/or the surgery performed to repair the defect damages the nerves. I was rushed to hospital and immediately given the last rites prior to being taken to theatre for surgery to close up the defect

I want to tell the story of the young lady who gave birth to me, who worried that I would not survive, but when I did, was determined that I would thrive, and that I would get every opportunity that I needed in life. That lady is Margarita Veronica Wilkinson. Rita.

When I was born we lived in a one bedroom council flat. Mam, Dad, brother and sister. Both supposedly normal, although I have my doubts.. Our bathroom was a tin bath in front of the fire and our outside toilet was shared between four families. I didn't live there long as the council decided (given my condition) we required better accommodation.

I survived that initial surgery, but it was some years before the full extent of my defect was determined. In Spina Bifida any of the lower nerves can be affected and so the results can be complex. I was 'lucky'. Whilst I walk - oddly, I was not paralysed, however, I am incontinent. I am unable to hold either urine or faeces and have no nervous impulse telling me to go to the toilet.

I know, I got off lightly, things could have been a lot worse. However, let's talk about the difficult subject of urine and faeces or to give it its vernacular - shit and piss. I'm sorry if I offend, but those are words that have followed me around for years and I am still ashamed of it. Why? Because I think as a society, we consider it dirty and disgusting, and that has been thrown at me my entire life. "Your smelly" "Your disgusting". So when I say my Mam made me visible, I meant that she determined that I would be regarded, considered.

Initially I didn't seem any different, after all none of us are born continent and with the ability to walk. In time it became clear that I was incontinent and had some issues walking. This is when my Mam took on the great task of her life - a cure for Spina Bifida, a task that would not end well. She tried many numerous and ultimately doomed treatments. Physiotherapy, surgery, acupuncture. Mostly, these treatments consisted of surgery to strengthen my bladder or to narrow the bladder neck. None of these treatments made any difference, but still she persisted.

My Mam is tiny, around 5ft tall with dark curly hair. She tells me that at the beginning she was thick, stupid, but she wasn't really, she just knew very little about my condition. However, she learned a lot and she quickly became able to question the specialists. She is a much tougher person than she thinks she is.

I had an invisible disability. Although I walked a little oddly, nobody could see my affliction or know that there was anything wrong with me. I tried to act as normally as possible. To this day, I would never use a disability toilet for fear of being called a charlatan and not disabled enough. Sometimes the hidden disability provokes interesting reactions from people. Many people when they first find out about my condition will say "Well you're alright, you're fine" without any real information to back up that statement.

Despite the fact that my issues were invisible, from the beginning my Mam had worked out that my life would be much more difficult if I was seen as different. She spent much time agonising about schooling. I could have gone to an ordinary school, but it was common in the sixties for those with a disability to go to a 'special school' that catered to their needs. She worried that she would get the decision wrong, she realised that I was likely to get a better standard of education in an ordinary state school, but she also reasoned that in a 'special' school the pupils would be supportive of each other. This turned out not to be the case, but in truth it was an impossible decision. How could she know what my life would be like once I walked through the school gates? In school there was a pecking order for disability and my issues with poo and pee made me stand out and I was frequently bullied.

In the background there was always my Mam, demanding that I be considered, that people cared for me. This small lady that had never fought for anything in her life, fought for me. In a world where women were encouraged to be meek and mild, she stood up to senior clinicians and teachers and demanded that they 'do something'. I think that the 'something' was often elusive, but the general idea was that I have as normal a life as possible.

How did that make me feel? In my younger years I would have loved to hide away, to not be noticed but my Mam wasn't like that and it was her assertiveness that taught me that I should stand up for myself. I watched her asking questions, trying to learn, thinking about new ways to help me, eventually getting there.

I look back on it with a sense of pride and I have adopted much of the same tactics myself. I want to be seen, I want to be heard.

My Mam made me visible. I think she did a good job.

A drawing of a Mazda by DK, the underdog of racecars

Someone who listened

by DK

My current consultant has been one of the few medical professionals that have listened to me, certainly with regards to my physical health, I still feel like I'm banging my head against the wall with the mental side still.

I have a pretty rare bone disease that isn't well understood and most of the medical community don't even know about at all, it's made my life hell. No one listened when I said I still had pain in my leg, I was often told I shouldn't still be in pain this long after a break in a condescending tone rather than an inquisitive one, and that I was just after the pills, a drug seeker. Many even said my pain was psychosomatic.

Eventually I was given a consultant that tried his best to listen to me but looked in all the wrong places unintentionally. He theorised what it could be but he wasn't a specialist on it, yet he still gave me his work mobile number if I needed to get in touch about anything. When he left his job at the Freeman he made sure I wasn't passed on to another oncology doctor but the only one who was a specialist in what he thought I might have, which turned out great for me. My new consultant took my concerns very seriously as I'd been going through this crap for nearly 11 years at this point and my year out if uni was fast approaching 7 years. I was given nuclear bone scans which showed what I had clearer than any scan I'd had before and showed a 6 inch benign tumour in the same place I'd been complaining of pain all these years.

The treatment I get is given once a year to old people with osteoporosis, I get it 4 times a year for pain management in an off the label treatment, even the nursing staff were out of their depth with the way I was given it. So when the pandemic hit it was cancelled, but I was scared as I'd massively reduced my oxycodone at this point and was worried I'd have no pain control indefinitely. I got in touch with him and said how worried I was and he was really apologetic, said it never should have been cancelled for FD patients and got me an appointment within the week.

At last, someone who listens

by Pat

After sixty five years with the same GP practice I finally believe I am being seen. As a person with feelings, worries and increasing needs for medical attention.

Over the years I have received help and treatment from all the doctors but have rarely seen the same one twice for any ongoing condition so was never able to build up a real relationship with someone which I am sure would have helped me when I was battling depression. This didn't matter after I retired in 2010, I was rarely ill, just the usual minor ailments that we all have from time to time.

This ended in 2021 when I joined a research trial for a vaccination and my blood pressure was found to be very high. I was also starting to have problems with mobility and beginning to feel very low. My first appointment was a telephone one with a doctor newly appointed to the practice. I held nothing back and he listened, with good humour I later realised. At last I had someone I could talk to who seemed to understand me and what I needed. This was followed up with a face to face meeting, he asked me what I liked to be called and I told him Pat, this made me feel valued. Medication was prescribed, he listened to my questions and answered them with an understanding of my worries.

On my fourth appointment I told him how much I valued having a named doctor and the continuity that went with it. Something I had never experienced before. He thanked me and said he also valued the chance to build a relationship with patients. I recently read that continuity of care has been proven to be greatly beneficial to patients, particularly older ones like me.

I really feel that at last I am seen.

The Greatest Gift

by NS

All she did was listen.
Listened with her open face.
The face that said it all –
"You're safe here.
It's your space
Use it how you want."

And then she said –
"Tell me how that feels, Louisa."
And that was all it took
For me to open up
In the comfort of her presence.

Nothing was too silly, too shocking, too shameful.
She gave me the unhurried space I needed
To bring out each feeling and unpack it.

All of it was validated.
I was validated,
I was important,
Every bit of me, every feeling.

She gave me the opportunity and the gift of saying it all.
Without shame and without judgement.
She handed to me the gift of compassion -
Of being compassionate to myself.
The greatest gift I have been given
And it has changed my life.

Who sees me

by Jean Angus

I have only one friend who knows what's going on in my life. That's my choice. I need someone I can talk to about the enormous changes I face. My solace.

I do feel invisible though. We met two consultants and an OT. My partner is the focus. Why not, she's facing something cataclysmic, for a short or long time, we don't yet know.

But life is turning, changing, shadows are looming and we can no longer predict much about our days. That is how it feels. I wake up and remind myself, today might be different.

My friend says " You may need help. I'll get some recommendations. I'm here but you may need a professional for you, for the family. Someone who understands the path you are on. The anger, the grief, the adjustments. You need help and support".

The consultants and healthcare are focussed on diagnosis, prognosis, a task, a patient. They don't see me, the impact. My friend sees me. She makes my role visible.

Being seen

by Maxine Patterson

Being seen at work, is only to be counted as a body so that no one has to cover your lessons. Yet when I was teaching, I looked at the young people and saw them; their eyes, sad, smiling, laughing, dazed. They saw me, "what's the matter, miss?" "Are those new earrings, miss?" But in the staff room, we didn't see anyone or anything. We sat, numbed and slowly regained strength to go and do it all over again!

Being seen at the Doctors: just another issue to be dealt with. Something minor, a nuisance, a follow up. And "Oh!" when she had to look because the thyroid was huge! Just occasionally she sees me, when she manages to squeeze some extra time at the end of an extraordinarily long day and we talk about my cancer and my son's suicide and yes; that time we see each other.

I was seen, looked at by the Endocrinologist at the local hospital after my first biopsy. Because I was a first! A rarity! He began to tell me what my cancer was, it had such a long name – I had to get a little notebook and write it down. He had to spell it out for me. And then; as an afterthought - what did I feel like? Did my symptoms conform?

I was seen, really seen by the oncologist at my first appointment. I was very ill and he stopped the ritual chat, he actually looked at me, made eye contact. I had to be admitted immediately, he said and continued holding my eyes and understanding what I was feeling. Even smiling at my incredulous questioning.

After that I was never seen, I became a package, a conveyor belt to be dealt with, operated upon. During many, many clinics and appointments I haven't been seen, just dealt with.

"A fully bloomed rose, because that's how I feel" — Gift

Blue Sky

by Gift

When I talk about my condition, the place where I am free to share about my condition is here in Blue Sky. Not out. The first person I met is Jill, she works here. I prefer if I've got problems, I come over here then we chat and someone solves. They can solve the problem.

2010. I heard it from RVI hospital. I was told by the doctors that you can go to Blue Sky because when you are there you can relax your mind and make some new friends.

And when I am here I am free to ask anything because I am not afraid because when you are here you are family. You all have the same condition. No one could talk about you because you are the same. So I am happy when I am here to discuss my problems because they keep it confidential. So they do not expose it. When you talk in here, it remains here. Inside here.

When I am here I feel at home. There are many things we do here. Like this time we are writing. It all relaxes my mind. That's why I like Blue Sky.

Doctor Smith

by AA

My only person I've ever trusted is Doctor Smith. He's such a lovely person. I was in hospital for a year. Some of the nurses were nasty to me. But he was always bringing jokes.

What happened was like, I tried to run away from the hospital and I came to the town. One thing I noticed, two police came because I was wearing the hospital gown. And they came, they said "Are you okay?"
And I say "yes"
"Where do you think you are going?"
"I'm going to Carlisle."
"Okay we will help you to take you to Carlisle." knowing it's the Doctors who phoned them that I ran away from the hospital and that if I collapse I can die so they have to find me.

Doctor Smith says "You have to put chains on her."
I remember when they take me to the hospital, I said "No I'm not getting out."
So they bring the bed, they tie me on the bed.
Once I entered Ward 19 everybody started laughing. I like fighting with the nurses. I start becoming annoyed. Like "Why are you laughing? What is funny?"
He say "AA, why did you want to go?"
I say "I'm going to Carlisle. I don't like it here."

Because I had been there for long time and one thing I hate being at the hospital was taking blood every single day, that make me more upset. If you are there every single moment they will come taking blood and I'd ask myself "What are they taking all this blood for?"
The doctor said "No AA, we have to check."
I say "Check what? All the blood you are taking you haven't checked what you wanted to check?"
Doctor Smith came he said "AA, you don't want them to take your blood?"
I say "No, no nobodys going to take my blood"
He say "AA we are just checking the virus-"
I say "Then let the virus kill me!"
He started laughing. He said "AA, do you want to die?
I say "Yes."

He said "If you die you will go back to Ghana"
So I have to give them the chance to take the blood.

So the woman in she comes.
I say "Um hm you. I don't like you. I have my own person I like."

So one nurse was very young. Vicky. She's very lovely. She was the only one who could give me some medication. That, I will take from her. The rest of them, I don't want to see their faces. Because the way they would behave towards us, like if they'd come to the room, how they would put gloves on and see me as not human. I remember one came there. I would ask if that woman is on duty, I will always want to cause problems. Because me and her, we can not stay for one minute. She'd behave as if I'm not a human being. You know, it's a reaction. Bring your spirit down. "If you want, eat. If you don't want, leave it."
So one day I just wake up and I say to her
"Look, are you Mother. And one thing I know for sure in life, what goes around comes around. Today it's me. It can happen to your grandchildren or your children. Sickness. Nobody wishes to get sick. So know how to talk to people because you are a mother, at the same time, you have to be a carer. Not being rude to people."

Sometimes the way people talk, they talk like they are the one helping you. Fine, I know I'm in a situation and I need to talk to people. But not to the extent of feeling bad. Like being in the hospital, nobody wishes to be there. So if you come there, you have to know how to talk to me. I know I'm in a situation, I'm dying, I need someone to encourage me not to come and ask me questions. That will be the last thing I will hate.

He's somebody who knows how to talk to people. There are people who are in this situation, all the women if you ask them; Doctor Smith. It's not like he's somebody, he's caring. Why only one person people keep on mentioning? He knows his way. I know he's working for money but he knows how to care. He's a very caring man. He knew what we are, it can happen to him.

When you want to talk to a blind person you have to behave like you are blind.

BST

by Isabel Marafao

When I was diagnosed it was 30 years ago. I remember that year.

I didn't know how to move myself in this country with all my health problems and chronic disease, HIV and Diabetes. I am so grateful for that help, it kept me going, like I am now. I'm so grateful for the care that she gave to me in all ways, physically and mentally.

I learned about BST through a psychologist at the RVI. I love that human, Jocelyn, she's now pregnant, she's happy, she helped me so much at the time. Because I had lost my right leg, I couldn't dance, I couldn't go to the beach. I couldn't do the things that made me happy a lot. She spoke to me about BST, so I came here. I am so grateful for that help, it kept me going, like I am now. I'm so grateful for the care that she gave to me in all ways, physically and mentally.

I started coming, meeting people from everywhere. Each one of those people I met, I observed them and I felt so much comfort. I have been coming for 5 years. I am a volunteer, a mentor and I help the people around me. That's what I love to do with my life.

We need the groups, because we are all afraid of one thing, of the same thing. But we are all together, we need groups to share, to learn from each other. We meet new people, artists, doctors, everybody. But we're still so protected and so supported. I used to say "Home, sweet, home" when I came here. I could just sit here and breathe. I feel so comfortable here, they show me the way to my health and my wellbeing. Because for me life is learning and the more knowledge I have the better. I'm so grateful for BST.

Anxious Minds

by Sarah Gunn

I saw the signs for Anxious Minds when I was walking through the shopping centre. I came before lockdown, I did mindfulness with Carol. We used to talk through things. It was really friendly, I felt like I could come in.

I haven't been to as many things since my partner died, I'm trying to get back into things. They died 3 months ago, but it's still helpful to come here.

My brother lives in Winchester, my other brother lived in Morpeth for awhile but I see my sister. I'm one of four, I'm the youngest.

I have counselling at the minute, through the NHS. She's a community psychologist, Francessca. She comes once a week. I've been seeing her for a month, she comes for half an hour. I went through my GP. The first time I went, they didn't listen, they refused to refer to me. I went back after the doctor left. I saw someone else and they sorted it out. The new GP takes me more seriously. It took about 6 weeks.

Nicole Nonhlanhla

Feeling Seen

by Nicole Nonhlanhla

Who made me feel seen?

Moving to Gateshead from Liverpool on the 16th of November 2019 was paramount.

I resided there under duress and affliction for three months. Subdued to the regimental rules of a man who challenged me in every way.

The leader came to converse with me after three months, to observe my fairing. I was in a conflict of interest with the armour bearer. The leader whom we called a Pastor put me to the side and actually spent time to find out about me

How I perceived everything and felt, he listened and supported what I had to say and he heard me. That was a pivotal moment that we were attached.

That is when I was approved, found validation, acceptance I craved for all my life. Arrived.

(Un)seen

by Hattie Eason

Me.

I see me for who I am and for all I feel,
No one else quite does, not completely, not for real.
I can't explain the pain to anyone at all,
It is simply hard to articulate whenever it is there, big or small.
And although my doctors have been great in more recent days,
I'm still wading through foggy areas caped in blacks, blues and greys.
But even with myself I can put up a wall,
Causing me to switch off my ears, causing me to fall.
I don't always listen to my body, my common sense or my mind,
I tend to brush aside what's best for me so I unravel and unwind.
It is in these far too often moments where I am more than alone,
For I am not there for myself and then low
    and behold my symptoms have grown.
So from now I need to listen to professionals and myself,
And avoid the cobwebs, the dust and the flies by not hopping
    back up on that shelf.

That was then, this is now

How has living with a health condition changed over time?

"Life is becoming narrower for me."

A new reality and the uninvited guest

by Steve Wood

This is now
By the twitching of my thumbs,
something wicked this way comes,
a tidal wave of tic and tremor,
the " can I move my foot" dilemma ,
falling from a standing start,
Laughing at the growing stain,
put away the constant pain,
you are the man whose mind is great,
but also he whose brain is always late,
to every party others love,
the severed hand in limpid glove,
the foot that twists,
the eyes that water,
the reminiscent well of laughter,
some days I am the man that was,
and then at times I am the motherfuckin boss.

This next is then
50 years,
Mild thrills, few spills,
I did my bit,
I paid my bills,
I loved my kids,
My partner too,
My course was set,
My aim was true,
My brain began to let me down,
Fewer smiles, far more frowns,
Pain and stiffness, left sided tremor,
Movement becoming a constant dilemma,
A "normal" day now tires me out.

12th December 2019, a Thursday,
My uninvited guest came to stay,
Turns out he'll never go away,
Messing with my brain, my pain, my walk and my talk,
All that is me has begun to fray.

Dreams

by Lynn

This morning I knew I had to come here today. I woke up at half five, and then I thought no going back to sleep. It's too early, I don't want to wake up then. It's been six o'clock the past three mornings. Then I woke up at half past seven and again I thought no I'll go back to sleep. Eventually I woke up at eight and felt totally groggy and it's taken quite a bit to pull myself together today. Normally I'm pretty chirpy, but it's just with all of these procedures I'm going through and stuff like that. Hopefully it'll come to nothing. Well, hopefully they can find out what's wrong and it'll put me right.

Going through these procedures does I suppose remind us of getting my HIV diagnosis. I remember when it actually happened. I went to the clinic which was in the general hospital then and I went there because I am a widow and had been sleeping around a bit. I was a widow when I was fifty and stupidly hadn't taken any precautions, so I thought well I better go check and I did. I remember the woman said- she was lovely, I remember her she was a nice big fat jolly woman and she said, 'yeah you are positive.' And I just sat there. She went 'No tears?'. I remember feeling well it's only one more thing to deal with.

What pisses me off is taking this medication, it just makes you feel so ill. You have to take medicine that empties your bowels before doing these procedures. I usually have a good relationship with medicine. I have angina which I take one pill in the afternoon and one at night-time and I take my HIV medication at nighttime. It's not something I think too much about, I just deal with it.

When I was first diagnosed with HIV, I had bad nightmares, which they warn you about. They were really vivid nightmares, where you wake up and still feel like you're in it.

I still have vivid dreams though, this morning I had a lovely dream. I was half awake and half asleep and I was telling myself 'I'm just here and I'm healing myself', and I think that's why I struggled to wake up this morning because it was so nice. I don't remember what the dream itself was like. Now my dreams are a beautiful space that I don't want to wake up from.

Life closing in

by Pat

I am looking back twelve years, 2010, I was aged sixty three and newly retired. Still on medication for the depression that had caused me to leave work sooner than I had planned but feeling hopeful for the next stage in my life. No aches or pains, the biggest problem was how I was going to fill my days.

But my life was closing in on me. My husband was ill for four years before he died in 2018, I had been his sole carer for all this time. I had to assist him physically to stand up or get out of bed and it was then that I first noticed the pain in my hands when he held on to them. My grip has gradually become weaker which affects mundane tasks like opening bottle tops or lifting pans from the stove. Now, when I buy such items I have to find someone to do this for me, child proof tops are impossible as I can't push the sides in while turning the lid. It makes me cross and I feel marginalised. One group of society mustn't open them, the other can't.

As a child I was always a bit round shouldered but nothing was made of it and it didn't stop me doing the things I wanted to. Looking back to working life I recall having to carry my heavy briefcase over my shoulder and wondering if this would cause me problems later. I don't know if it did contribute to the stoop that developed gradually over my later years but nothing I can do about it now. Walking any distance leaves me breathless, the physiotherapist I was sent to told me it was simply that I was hunched over causing my lungs to be constricted. She gave me exercises which have not helped. So now I use a walking stick and walk more slowly. And feel old. And embarrassed. Going out anywhere with friends is problematic as it is natural to chat as you walk along and I can't do this as I need all my breath just to keep me going.

Life is becoming narrower for me, I have had to give up going on outings or to events where walking or even standing for any time is needed. I miss this aspect of my life greatly as I had joined in everything that was offered. I can no longer keep my small garden in order, change a light bulb or reach some of the shelves in my kitchen. Routine tasks like changing the bed or hanging out the washing leave me breathless. I have to sit at the kitchen bench to prepare my meals. Employing people to do things I once could is stressful and expensive but I no longer have a choice.

In one way I suppose I am lucky, I have all the disability aids in place and when I use them I think of Michael and how he needed them too. I haven't started to use his stair lift or mobility scooter but they are ready for me.

When the time comes.

Diagnosed

by Pauline Hass

When I first got diagnosed, I was very, very angry and was banging my head against a brick wall, trying to figure out where I got it from. It took a while for me to figure it out. Think it happened one night, when out of the blue, my sister, Sandra called and asked me if I want to go to her friend's wedding, which was the Saturday. I wasn't doing anything that weekend and didn't have a partner in my life at that time. So Sandra picked me from my place on Saturday morning and later on we went to the wedding which was held I think at the couple's house. Very small wedding.

This guy started speaking to me and we spent most of the evening together. Didn't know him from Adam. A complete stranger. Then he asked me to go home with him. I said no a few times. He practically begged me. So I eventually I gave in. He was a friend of the bridal couple. So I kinda trusted him. So I told my sister I was going home with him. I was drunk. First time I ever did this. So the following morning he took me home. We kept in contact for a short while. He was going away on his December holidays. So just left it at that. None of us contacted each other again. So first time in my darn life I have a one night stand and I get HIV. I didn't realise it at that time because I was diagnosed a few years later. Only symptoms I experienced was I used to get flu like symptoms, mostly sniffles just before and after my periods. I thought this was normal, because it lasted until I was diagnosed. Not knowing it was HIV. All the times I used to go to Doctor before being diagnosed, not once did they do a blood test. Suppose it wasn't necessary at the time.

Fast forward to today. The anger has lessened a lot. Just take my tablet automatically every night. Most days I forget I have it. The only thing is, none of my family members know. There is very few people that know. My husband, my best friend Cheryl, and my previous Team Leader and previous Manager that I used to work with.

Sometimes, Jorn and I have a conversation about whether to tell my children and my oldest sister Judith. During these conversations, I always freeze and my brain tells me not to tell them.

I am not sure why I never told my family in the beginning of me being diagnosed. All I know is that Judith is a worrier and 71 years old and she has her own health issues and family problems, so at this stage I cannot tell her. Can't add my burdens onto her. My daughter, Tanya is still in South Africa. It would be unfair to tell her on the phone or video call. Sylvester is in the UK with his family. I often baby sit for them.

But I want all my children to be present, one day if I do tell them.

Mark Barham

Dying? Not a chance

by Mark Barham

I am taking you back around 24 years ago. I was on quadruple HIV therapy and unable to work due to all the different side effects, nausea, night sweats, and being high on the tablets. I was able to apply for Disability Living Allowance, now it's called PIP. I was advised my DS1500 would help, I was confused what this form was and how I was to obtain one.

An appointment at my GP surgery would give me these answers. This was one of the most shocking pieces of news I have ever been given.

My doctor advised me that as I was diagnosed HIV positive, I would not live past 30 years old, I was 25 at the time. He then explained what the DS1500 was, basically it says you have 6 months or less to live. You also get them for cancer as well.

Being told this is kind of weird, you don't want to accept it and you don't believe it. So many of my friends were dying around this time and I was scared. I only had just lost my sister 2 years previously, she was murdered in the Philippines, so I was still very fragile from that.

I was upset more about this than I was after the news of my sister. I didn't go out much, only to the local HIV support centre which was LEAN back then London East Aids Network. I had some amazing friends which helped a lot.

I had not told my parents of my diagnosis at this point, partly not wanting to put more worry on them. So I dealt with the news with the help from friends, so I was not alone. I thought I might want to do things before I die, like hot air ballooning or seeing Australia. But how the hell was I going to do it all? I wanted to stay positive, I have never been a depressed kind of person.

So I applied for a few credit cards, after getting DLA the credit card companies took that as income so they were willing to give them to me. I had about 6 and maxed them all out, I thought what the hell, I thought I would be dead soon and won't have to pay them back. How wrong were the medical professionals and I.

The pills started to work and my viral load, the amount of the virus in your blood, went from over a million and half down to undetectable. My 30th birthday came and went and I was still alive, this I was glad of. Even though I was well my DLA was not taken away as it was given for life, at that point.

Then and now

by Violet Rook

In the 1980's my parents died within three months of each other.

I remember standing over the grave of my mother with my Dad, he and I both knew how ill he was, and I could see in his eyes what he was thinking. Of course this was repeated when I stood alone after his demise.

Both died of cancer. I had nursed my mother, getting her oxygen cylinders regularly to help her breathe. Then my Dad who despite vomiting a lot kept going for his wife's sake until he finally lost hope when she died.

I wonder what they would think now and what they would think about the pandemic. Despite the distance in time, many aspects of care have not changed. It still remains the luck of the draw, what care one receives and often depends on where one lives and one's demographic area. Ageism and class play a big part in healthcare. But now these are strengthened by the use of algorithms used to diagnose illness.

When one rings up any department one is aware of the algorithmic processes used to distinguish patients. If one answers yes to a question or no, the answer will result in a differing aspect of care.

The next development will be more use of Artificial Intelligence or AI, and this does not just mean robots.

My skin and me

by Jean Angus

Summertime and choices must be made
My longest trousers and dresses
To disguise my spotty distresses

No more shorts and minis
No more shapely legs
My younger liberty
The envy of my aged cage

I debated giving up the things that I love
To glide in the water
To freely move
But find that I am resilient yet

I cannot shake my conscious self
But age has given me a thicker edge
To brood about my skin and former nature
Is a woeful and bitter response

I know what is harmful to my mental state
I shake my fist at the world
Just like my younger mate

My spots are scars
My suit of armour
Wear with honour
And ignore the horror.

No drugs, no cure

by Mary O'Sullivan-Fawcett

Our blood ran cold
Not only had we been given the worst diagnosis possible We'd been given a
death sentence
And informed that there was no cure at all, no options

At least you normally got a "we'll start with this and, if that doesn't work, there
are other options"
These though were the chilling facts, one tablet to maybe give you one month
on a year but it was not totally clear if it did do that, or worked in any way, at
least we got truth

Your body will shut down, "we can't say how slowly"
Prognosis. Your life span from now is between three and five years

The tests to confirm the diagnosis had been brutal
Doctors had offered to do them quickly, they knew what the results would be
Done over five days, admission to hospital but home every night
Where we would hold onto each other whispering our love and saying we'd get
through it Whatever it was

On day six we arrived on the ward but it was as though a switch had been
pulled No-one met our eyes, the smiling, cheerful nurses were gone
They carried themselves differently, spoke in soft, almost reverent tones
Left us alone with a blackening cloud over our heads

So we knew before the consultant even spoke to us it would be bad

What we didn't know was that there was nothing that could ease suffering
Could slow down the progress of the disease
That making life as easy as possible was the only thing to be done
We would be gently enfolded into a clinic, we didn't really want, that would see
us through

And so it began.

Diagnosis, the Golden Ticket

by Tony Moore

Then.

Before my diagnosis of Autism, I was a different person. I knew what I had. I knew how it affected me. At times I loved myself. I owned and indeed loved my Autism. I didn't really need to know my Autism too well to fall in love with it. Autism was defining me and what is there not to love about me? It is also true though, that before my diagnosis, despite not needing to know too much about my Autism for my own self-esteem and self-worth, others seemed to be fascinated and indeed needed to know more than I knew. This was most visible and indeed most audible in the workplace. Then, I was put into a dark scary place. I could not, and indeed should not have had to explain myself. I had come out as "gay" in a world where nobody needs to come out as "straight" Why should I also be required to come out as "Autistic?"

I panicked, I overthought things. Self-Harming, which had been a coping mechanism, indeed a friend I had control over for most of my adult life now started to take a more dominant and dangerous backdrop to my life. My self-esteem and self-worth were stretched to their limits.

Now.

My diagnosis has given me a script. I can use this script to explain myself to others, to explain myself to myself. To understand myself. To fall back in love with and own my Autism and to love myself again.

This is now. This is the future.

Life batteries depleted

by Dr Larry Gurney

HIV in the late eighties/early nineties.

It was scary in some ways. Why? I would say because of the unknowns but ironically the known was the fact that there was a diagnosis. Three years to live as things were.

But somehow that was useful as I had just had cancer a year or so earlier that didn't kill me. I'd just lost my son so futures were not too happy feeling.

So I decided to throw myself into speaking out. Doing something positive. Three years of 100% all rules gone. Yeah I could do that with purpose. Activism. Surrounded by people.

But then I didn't die. And now living with HIV, I can do nothing special. I can make little or no contribution. Now I feel more lost because I am found.

But what I've got left with is the product of what I gave up. That was normal. I'm bored because I used up all my batteries running on 100%.

Just alone.

A time I felt...

Writing about the emotions we attach to memories.

"Don't give it up. You carry on. Things will get better.
Nothing stays the same for long."

Six weeks I will never forget

by Pat

My memory is of the six weeks I spent on a mental health ward after I finally admitted to myself that I needed more help than outpatient appointments and medication alone could give me for my depression. I had walked out of work the previous day as I could not cope with anything. I told no one, just left and rang my psychiatrist for help.

This was over twenty five years ago and I should have known what to expect as I was an approved social worker well used to admitting people to such wards, often compulsorily. I was so wrong, it was nothing like the ones I had worked on.

My husband Michael took me into the ward, I was shown into a lounge that was heavy with smoke where everyone stopped looking at the television and looked at me instead. I ran out and cried. Someone took me to my room but gave me no information about what was to happen or offered any comfort. I sat there alone for several hours and started writing a diary. I can't read it now, it is still too painful.

I felt forgotten as indeed I had been, my evening meal was the biscuits and water I had brought with me. I suppose I could have gone in search of someone but stubbornness kept me there, waiting to see how long it would be before I was noticed. Finally someone came, it was medicine time. I was taken to the trolley where I overheard a nurse asking where the social worker was. I felt stigmatised. I had a name.

Things slowly got better, I became used to the routine and I made friends with another patient who accepted the help and understanding from me that I had not received. It made me feel good to be needed again and we stayed in touch after we both went home.

I had been given a named nurse but rarely saw her and there was little in the way of treatment or therapy. Luckily I was allowed to return home for weekends but going back was hard. I believe that having no responsibilities for anything and freedom from work stress was the treatment I needed to recover.

I had told very few people where I was, those I did supported me with visits and phone calls for which I was very grateful even though I felt uncomfortable at them seeing me in those surroundings.

Returning to work a few months later was strange, I had a new manager who was clearly ill at ease with me, luckily he was soon 'promoted' and I settled back into my team. I felt better able to understand the fears of some of my clients and to support them in their journeys through hospital treatment and into recovery. There was some good to come from my experience.

Fatal Whimsy

The Mirror

by Fatal Whimsy

As I turn to wash my hands I freeze.
There she is in the mirror:
The undead.
She's come back for me, just as I'd feared she would.

She's feasting on my brains.
She's feasting on my body.
Pale, like she's ill, but she does not have the flu.
Her hair sticks together, matted in greasy oil.
Her eyes protrude from the gaping hollows above her cheekbones.
She isn't dead, but stares,
empty.

I feel her inside me.
She is destroying me.
She has starved me.
Now my stomach is digesting me.
Nausea takes over.
There is nothing left for her to feed on.

I can't move,
She scares me.
I can't scream,
She stops me.
I am all alone.
It's just me,
Her,
And the mirror.

I feel weak.
I long for my bed,
The safety of my comfortable bed,
Where nothing can harm me.
Except her!

Ripples of Doom

by Steve Wood

A storm raged silently
At it's centre, the smallest blemish on an ink black pupil
I contemplate what this will mean for me, focused, still,
What do I do, now I know I am ill?,
Of course I took the news like a man
With a dose of equanimity and solid, British chin,
And now I'm doing all I can,
To ensure my fears will not get in
If I allow the dam to break
I fear what route my mind may take
If I describe this thing I'm feeling
Whose peace of mind will I be stealing?
Furious, Fearful, Curious, Tearful

I will not be the object of your pity
The whispered subject of prurient sorrow
It won't be pleasant, it won't be pretty
But I will be the master of my own tomorrow
Yet despite my clam shell resolution
My stubborn mask of stalwart, British constitution
My eyes betray the truth of things
Fear and uncertainty driving me to angry exclamation
To shrill and ever more unfair remonstration
With those I love the most

My doubts and fears
My self-recrimination
Given shape in dark and dangerous ripples
Ink dark waters given weight by my hidden tears
Mortality is looming
A sudden intimation of my hopelessness
The harsh, internal taunts of " cripple"

The longer I am silent
The more they are concerned
The more they ask me to unload
The more I feel my old self burned
Man of straw, set a fire to appease the gods
To rise again maybe, defy the odds?
But then the trip, the fall, the tremor
The shakes, the wobbles, covering shame with the darkest humour
"Get in there first, before the normals do"
Before those bastards take the piss, just like...well, like I asked them to...
The languid ripples of my self doubt
Become a raging Tsunami
The incoherent howl of fury and self pity that must out
Threatening to drown those who love me
Each time I cry, or wail, or shake or shout.

Nicola Spain

Thank you, Mum

by Nicola Spain

It's inevitable, as sure as night follows day. Every single time.
Hovering in readiness, poised for the precise moment it can leap into action.
A coiled spring, about to unravel at the slightest movement.
I'd bet my savings on it and make millions - certain of the outcome.
All it takes is for me to pop my head around her bedroom door
And her face breaks into a huge smile.

'Thank you, Darling' she says gently
    as I help her into fresh pyjamas after her bath.
'Thank you, Sweetheart' she whispers
    as I carefully move the brush through her silky hair.
'Thank you, Precious' she gasps
    as I wipe the corner of her mouth with a soft tissue.
'Thank you, Louisa', I have to strain to hear her voice, as I kiss her goodnight.

And now it's my turn.
'Thank you, Mum for making it so easy to care for you, as your heart overflows
with gratitude at every little thing we did for you. Even in sickness you made
things as easy for us as you possibly could.'

Hoofbeats

by Maxine Patterson

I felt mad at the start of my Neuroendocrine Cancer journey, because almost every doctor and consultant at hospitals discounted my symptoms. The arrogant complacency: "you have IBS." This misdiagnosis and refusal to think of other diseases and cancers applies to almost every other Rare Cancer patient I have met; either face to face or all over the world, via zoom meetings on the internet.

Patients are just numbers to make up a list. Going through that list is a process, numbers to be ticked off during a clinic. Patients are not supposed to talk, to present symptoms that don't fit with well known, preconceived ideas of what is wrong. Consultants who know better certainly don't make any pretence of listening to the patient who can actually explain what their symptoms are.

The symbol of a Rare Cancer is a Zebra. I didn't understand this, until various Doctors and Nurses explained that Doctors' training instils into them, if they hear hooves, they should think of horses. Rare Cancer organisations ask that they should also consider other causes; rarer cancers, hooves can also sound like Zebras.

Even an internationally famous Oncologist in America who is also a Neuroendocrine Cancer patient had to struggle quite forcibly to overcome the suggestion that he was being a hypochondriac. So, if someone who has power and authority is not taken seriously, what hope is there for us ordinary people?

So, it took over six long, long years to be diagnosed; then suddenly everything happened at once. Massive operation, long recuperation and then what? Learning to live with Neuroendocrine Cancer.

In a way, that's why my list of Sad things was so much longer than my Mad list. If you have to live with Cancer, the first and hardest stage is to learn to accept. Because if you don't, you're angry and disgruntled at everything, at the Cancer, at not being well, at having horrible symptoms, at having to have monitoring scans, and having to change your life in a major way. That doesn't mean you go around like Pollyanna, finding the positive in everything. Because, quite frankly, there isn't always a positive.

So my Sad list contained many of the aspects of my life that cause me concern, make me think, change the way I have to live: living to the clock so that I remember to take my tablets. Planning the diary so that the essential Somatastin Analogue injection can be ordered, and delivered and carefully stored in the fridge. At over a £1,000 a dose it's an important responsibility. That injection keeps my tumour under control, but of course like everything, there are side] effects. Learning to cope with terrible sleep; sad that I have to be so careful with what I eat and sad that quite often my moods are so volatile that I am short tempered and very grumpy with my long suffering husband.

It's no good being mad at those aspects of my life, because they are actually the things that are keeping me reasonably well and allow me to live a reasonable life.

One of the first things I remember the Specialist Nurse; actually Wonder Woman in disguise; emphasising was the importance of acceptance. I heard her words as I sat with head bowed sobbing uncontrollably at my first patient support meeting. Now I understand those words and try to live by them, hence my long list of sad things.

My glad list is short, but massively important; my garden. Getting out in the fresh air, seeing wildlife and being a part of something living and vital.

Mary O'Sullivan-Fawcett

Two Sides

by Mary O'Sullivan-Fawcett

Cautious footsteps
A soothing voice
Gentle hands
Eyes full of questions
And the hurt goes both ways
Are met with rage
Frustration and anger
Eyes screaming with pain
A voice scratched and barely there

Each knows and understands the other
The encounter leaves them both bereft
With tears flowing
Slowly one leaves the room

After a while a return is made
A door opens, eyes meet
Falling into open arms
With calming words of love

Caring is a two way street
Not always easy on either side
But with tenderness and love
A path among the obstacles can be made

Anxious

by Rosie

A time when I was anxious was when I had to visit my new school as I was nervous about moving.

I was scared they weren't going to like me or that I was so nervous I'd do something stupid and embarrass myself.

There was a lot of new people to meet which I found very scary, and I wanted to make a good impression, as moving meant a lot to me and my family but I didn't want to let them down, it felt like a lot of pressure on me.

Meeting the first teacher was really scary and I could feel myself shaking while I was talking to him.

Luckily he was really nice.

I relaxed a bit until he took me on a tour of the school.

To be brave

Bravery is an interesting concept. Do you feel brave?

"Not brave, coping, managing, sometimes not managing; but still alive."

Distractions

by Maxine Patterson

Why should I feel brave? Bravery implies some sort of chosen response; but living with Neuroendocrine Cancer doesn't allow choices. There's treatment and medication combined with the daily routines of everyday life. Everyday life is not brave, it's mundane and boring, with enjoyable intervals. What to wear, what to eat, where to shop, how to manage the money, what to watch on television.

However, there's the garden! Weeding, pruning, being out in the fresh air, listening to the birds and insects, revelling in the profusion of flowers, sheer pleasure.

Living with Cancer loads everyday life with extra issues, medication, injections, Doctor's appointments; if you're lucky; scans, blood tests. But I am here, living with Cancer, so how lucky am I?

Not brave, coping, managing, sometimes not managing; but still alive and kicking!

Living with Neuroendocrine Cancer isn't brave, what it takes is determination. The first and most important phrase the specialist nurse stressed at an early Natter Meeting was the importance of acceptance. Acceptance of Cancer allows you to live with it and make the most of life.

The old brown bench

by E Lee

I am glad the sun is out. It always adds to the mood for those who pass by, sit and ponder here. I have encountered many tears from those who choose to sit on me.

Oh. She is back and she looks...

I have seen her before. I think she was putting on a brave face before.

She has told someone on the phone that
"It's returned"
and then she quickly followed that statement with
"It's fine, I'll be fine."

It's okay to not be okay and to say you are not okay. It is also okay to cry no matter where you are in the journey of cancer. It's not brave to hold it all in or not talk about cancer. Talking helps you process it. As hard as it is for me to say Cancer will be with you for the rest of your life. But you will learn how to dance in the rain, sing a new song and how to laugh and smile again.

It's fine to sit and breathe. It's also fine to be vulnerable, sad, happy, joyful, angry, hopeful, teary and strong.

Life has changed, but don't let cancer rob you of living the life you want to live..

If I was

by DK

People often infer that I'm brave living and dealing with chronic pain, however I have no choice in the matter, I think you'd need to be braver to choose not to live. If I was so brave, why would I spent most of my life trying to run from it? The drug abuse? The self harm?

There is a fine line between bravery and stupidity. In my late teens you could say it was brave of me to get behind the wheel while I was living in another reality and on painkillers that made morphine look like calpol, I wasn't in control of my mind, yet I still got behind the wheel and drove at silly speeds.

I thought I was quite brave when I got forced into a corner and had to ask someone out, a long and strange story. For someone like me who is shy and had never done anything like that I was proud of how brave I was. But with my mental and physical health I don't feel brave, its took me 15 years to finally speak to my doctor about it as I was worried I'd be locked up.

Even today I get up not knowing what's real and what isn't and it scares me, so no I don't feel brave.

Proud to stand out

by Liz Gregson

I don't feel brave: there isn't a choice
I do what I need to overcome
barriers, achieve my aspirations
and have a voice
to lead a full, active life.

When I was younger I was teased
last to be chosen for the team
on the sidelines. Excluded
because of my eyesight felt mean
but I had to move on.

I tried to avoid mentioning sight
How could I talk about a condition
I didn't really understand?
Later I found out more about it
and was able to comprehend.

Trying to avoid complaining
I became confident challenging
barriers I encountered.
Tactfully I tried explaining
to achieve realistic expectations.

Some people's lack of understanding
when I miss seeing something
can lead to harsh comments.
I either ignore them or reply.
Apologise, then wonder why?

No one has called me brave.
When people compliment me
I'm surprised, but pleased.
I no longer feel concerned
about appearing different.

I'm now proud to stand out.

Elaine

Older and braver

by Elaine

Some people don't like injections at all. Some people pass out at the very thought of an injection. I belong to the "Oh just get on with it" category. Well, I used to belong to that category. Macular degeneration is a common cause of central vision loss among people aged 60 and over. So, I have had to accept that biologically and actually I am an "older" woman. If I wasn't "older" I wouldn't be getting this thing at all. There is no cure for getting older or for macular degeneration. But the hospital documentation tells me that there are treatment options that may slow the progression of the disease. OK – so now I have a disease too. A disease which is not going to go away but which can be made to progress more slowly. Macular degeneration becomes "wet" when abnormal blood vessels grow and bleed & leak fluid in the back of the eye. Note that I said abnormal no problem there – I was never normal and "eye", that indicates one eye. Oh no, not me. I have this wet stuff in both eyes.

Medical science is amazing. They have come up with some magic that can block the abnormal blood vessel growth & fluid leakage and I know that no-one wants fluid leakage. So, all good then. If I get some of this "stuff" maybe I won't have a dark, empty area in the centre of everything that I look at. Colours may not seem as faded. My vision may not be blurred. Maybe I shall see straight lines instead of wavy lines. I could maybe read a book that isn't "large print", or read the channel information on the tv listing. Maybe even get my driving licence back. They say that this magic may maintain or even improve my vision. So, all the above is possible.

Living with sight loss makes you realise how doggedly determined you need to be to achieve the simplest thing. How much longer everything takes to do or how many things have to change to be done at all. Some things will never be done again. Bravery doesn't come into it. You have to do what you have to do. I used to have authority in my life, now I have as much authority as a Do not tumble dry label.

I have had injections in my arms, my thighs and my buttocks. And everywhere else you could stick a needle. But never, ever had I been told to lie back whilst each eye is numbed and disinfected with drops & then a "tool" placed on my eye to stop me from blinking, and I am told to keep my head very still as the Doctor puts the needle into my eye and injects the magic fluid. I can feel slight pressure and can see the bubbles from the liquid. I don't breath and I hang onto the sides of the bed as though my life depends on it. When both eyes are done I stand up slowly and thank the staff for the treatment and say how grateful I am for their skill & magic and silently pray that this unnatural torture is worth it. I think that is brave. And I do it again every 6 weeks. I wouldn't wish it on my worst enemy.

Conversation formulas

by Victoria Gray

Ah, the British obsession with the weather.
We're part of unique phenomenon discussing the weather like we do.
It's part of the British culture.
Our fallback in a conversation.
Smoothening conversation utterly butterly.
It's similar to scenarios where someone is called brave.
Often we respond to terrible news with 'brave'.
A response formula.
Allowing us to recognise someone's hardship whilst granting ourselves
    a filler sentence to digest what we've just been told.

Operation
by Rosie

A few years ago I had to have an operation, and everyone kept telling me how brave I was.

Although they were all being nice I found it quite patronising, as I didnt feel brave; these people were not giving me a choice on whether or not I had the operation, I had to for my health.

Given a choice, I wouldn't go through with the operation, which didn't feel much like bravery to me. The word brave gives me very mixed emotions because people call me brave after everything I've been through with the intention of kindness but I feel as though it is not necessarily the right word to use. At no point did anyone give me a choice to go through hard times.

Had I chosen to do it, that would make me brave, but I never chose it or decided it: it just happened. Because of this, I don't feel like brave fits me well. I prefer the word strong as it represents me better.

You're so brave

by Lynn

You know a lot of people say that to people with different conditions, you know if you have cancer 'oh you're so brave'. It's not bravery, it's just something you get on with day to day: sometimes you have good days, sometimes you have bad days. So yeah, we're not braver than anybody else, it's just something you must cope with.

People don't tell me that I'm brave. I know through other people, like my friend who has cancer and everybody says to her 'oh you're so great,' or 'you're so brave' and she's thinking she's not, she's just going through it. Bless her. and I know if people did say that to me I'd say 'well scuse you I'm not, I'm just going through it!'

'Oh, you're so brave'. Patronising, it's easy to say.

Everybody goes through things, as I said when I was diagnosed with HIV 'It's just another thing to go through- you know, just another thing to go through.

People just go through the things they go through, I don't feel that I'm braver than anybody else, you know what I mean?

I'd want to educate people to know not to say 'oh you're so brave'. Like what I was saying about my friend with cancer, bless her, she is brave, I think she's brave. But at the end of the day it's just something she goes through and copes with it

I have a procedure tomorrow, which I had to take the medication for today. I was thinking about not coming but, but so far I haven't had any adverse effects and I thought it was good to come in and be with people, rather than mulling things over on my own. But I suppose when you go through a procedure- it's what you say to kids 'oh you're very brave'. We are brave I suppose but I don't feel it that way.

Bravery

by David Oliver

Bravery is what you make of it. It could be getting out of bed that day. Finally getting around to that thing you've been trying to do for weeks. Or it could be continuing, in spite all you face and the knowledge that things may never change. You take things one day at a time and you see how things go. You carry on and you give a big old middle finger to the brain that's working against you. You go forward, trying not to look back and you try and be the best version of yourself that you can be.

You shout from the rooftops about your experiences. Good or bad, you just keep trying. History has a way of telling you that bravery is this big bold statement. And it's sometimes far from it. Sometimes it's the little things that matter. Those little steps towards everyday normality. Pushing through the Depression, anxiety and the brain fog. It's making sure you take care of yourself even though you think you don't deserve it. Its facing adversity. It's leaving the house. It's walking down the street. It's being yourself. It's telling yourself to face one more day. It's telling yourself that everything is going to be okay.

It's continuing on despite everything. It's existing, it's stressful. It's *bravery*.

Barry Wilkinson

Don't call me brave

by Barry Wilkinson

Is a blind man brave for walking the street?
Is a deaf woman bold for going to work?
Is navigating a wheelchair through a doorway brave?
Is walking with callipers heroic?

Don't call me brave
I live my life
Don't call me brave
Because I face some strife
Call me lucky

Have you had my life?
Walked my walk?
Seen the things I've seen?
I'm not brave, I'm lucky
I am the privileged one
I am the honoured

Bravery

by Fatal Whimsy

Mental illness. It's not like other long term illnesses. You aren't often seen as brave for surviving. For living on without throwing yourself off a bridge, or for not joining the 27 club.

You're more likely to be portrayed as weak. If stigma tells you that enough, you feel it too. I definitely feel weak. I also feel ashamed.

In some ways, yeah, maybe I am strong, maybe even brave-ish. Some of the stupid shit I've done to get out stress, is probably brave, but not really because at the time, I didn't know what I was doing.

I know I've come a long way, since my recklessness and danger seeking behaviours. From the days when I was furiously fuelled by intrusive, racing and all-consuming thoughts. I know I've achieved some things that people may say are impressive or take guts and strength to achieve. I feel more in control now, that's definitely something to feel good about. Still, I can't help but feel like 'bravery' is more of an imposter and that 'survivor' may be a better suited description for me.

The falling angel

by Steve Wood

Before I was disabled, I was disabled,
I just didn't know it,
Before I wrote poetry, I didn't write poems,
But I was a poet,

So when my doctor told me,
That my brain was conspiring with my body,
To cause me maximum, enduring strife,
And I'm mentally bowed and bloody,
My inner self screaming " Fuck my life!",
The fact that I remain here,
Relearning who I am now,
Doesn't mean I want your tears,
Or whatever plaudits you allow,
I've more tears than enough,
And no, I'm not especially tough,
Day after day of being me,
Is not an act of bravery,
I'm not plucky, or lovely, I don't seek to inspire,
I do not possess an unquenchable fire,
I grow tired, I get ratty,
My wings are dirty, my halo tatty,
I will whinge, I will bitch,
'bout my middle life glitch,
So please don't tell me how brave I must be,
Cos' I don't have a choice, and you don't know me.

I'm Not Brave

by Hattie Eason

I don't feel brave, in fact I feel quite the opposite.

Although I wear a mask each day, I am no hero, no strong inspiring woman.

I am scared and I am frustrated.

I am hurting and I am beyond tired.

I am a thirty year old woman in a body which feels older than it should be; it feels worn, stiff and never ready to take on whatever gets thrown at it, nor does my mind.

There are cobwebs a-plenty which can't simply be wafted away with a feather duster.

I'm still figuring this out and haven't got on top of it yet.

I am still going back and forth between the GP and the specialists.

I am still awaiting physiotherapy and seeing a therapist.

I have a long way to go to heal and recoup.

That's not to say I'll be rid of this, there is no getting rid of this.

But I know I can get better, be better, feel somewhat better.

I just want a little better.

So, no.

I'm not brave.

Not brave.

No.

The Ripple Effect

Imagine your condition as a raindrop and your life is
a body of water, what kinds of ripples has it caused?

"There are many ripples. Even ripples within ripples."

Ripples

by Barry Wilkinson

There are many ripples. Even ripples within ripples. I was born and Mam dedicated her life to my preservation. Dad struggled to understand my condition, we had a difficult relationship, distant. My brother looks at me and calls me heroic, stoical, in reality I am merely living a life, my life. My whole family have worried about me.

I attended a school with a curriculum for those who have physical disabilities and/or special educational needs, and are frequently absent. The education is limited. I do ok, but I don't feel clever enough to attend University. I have a lifelong educational inferiority complex. This ripples into my desire to see my children attend University. Ripples within ripples. My children. I was told that given the surgery that I had, I would be unlikely to have children. I have two incredible boys, men now. My love for them is stronger because they seemed like my own special miracles.

Many of my school friends are now dead. The Cystic Fibrosis, the Hydrocephalus, the Muscular Dystrophy, the Asthma. Eventually, most of them succumbed to their maladies. I think of them often

My nursing career. I thought it a random decision, now I see that it was a choice made from personal experience. My first student placement ends with a poor report. "Lazy" "Slow" "Not able to keep up" was fine, but "Maybe this is because he has a physical disability" was too much, a step too far, and I started working harder, walking faster, doing more. I moved around a lot in my career into different roles, different specialities, not because I was brave but because I got scared as I went up the ranks and I ran away. The old inferiority complex kicking in.

Ripples. I struggled to find a girlfriend. As I got older and sex raised its head I was terrified. I didn't want to disrobe, share my body with anyone. I was terrified of smelling or being incontinent or just looking abnormal. To this day I use unwarranted amounts of after shave. It's a tiny ripple. When I got a girlfriend I was intense, practically declaring undying love and proposing after a few dates. I was a teenage prude, there were no wild oats sown from my direction.

I fell in love with my wife partly because I could see that she was strong where I was weak and that she would push me and support me. Without her I would be so much less than I am, with her I am so much more than I was. I remain a work in progress. There are times my wife has become my carer and that changes your relationship in a bad way, so you try hard not to be that person that cries out for help and worries people. As I said I remain a work in progress.

My boys have grown up in a household of illness. I wonder what that was like? I often feel unwell, I can have severe infections. The boys rarely react when told I am unwell, not because they are uncaring, but because they are used to this life. Had I been healthier would the children have had a different upbringing? A ripple. When I am unwell I sometimes wonder if my symptoms are really *that* bad. I have often wished for the ability to cast my symptoms into someone else, just for a short while, not because I am cruel but just so I can check "Is that as bad as I think?" and then I would take the symptoms back.

Looking back over this writing it seems so terrible, but in reality, in the words of Clarence the guardian angel, I have really had a wonderful life. My condition has made me the man that I am, and I like myself. I know that my family loves and cares for me. I may not have had the best education but in my school I learned the value of listening and caring for others, never prejudging, seeing the person and not the wheelchair - so to speak. I am someone that hates injustice or bigotry in any form. My kids and have grown into fantastic people and I had something to do with that. I made the right career choice, I ran away from certain things but I also found myself running towards others and through that I have travelled the world, had many great experiences, met many lovely people. So there are many, many ripples but they are not all bad, they are just the experiences that make you. I would never wish my condition away because then I wouldn't be me. Still, I do quite fancy the power to cast my symptoms into someone else though.

David Oliver

The Ripple Efffect

by David Oliver

I expect you want to hear about the effects of this thing with me, don't you? I'm afraid it's more complex than that. Not quite as simple. I was first diagnosed at aged 23. A very Late Diagnosis for autism indeed. Nevertheless, it answered a lot of questions. Why I processed things differently. Why I couldn't quite get things right. And why I felt like a piece of the puzzle that didn't quite fit.

At first it was relief. There was finally an answer to all those niggling questions. I could finally start to piece myself together. A pile of broken fragments with no particular order. It was up to me to make it my own. To figure out where and when things went. To find a sense of purpose and prepare myself for unlocking the secrets.

To this day I still feel the same way. I'm still figuring out new things about my brain, and what co-exists with the condition. A feeling I have been feeling and thing about since initial diagnosis. Because it's such a large mine field of exploration, I'm still figuring it out, learning new things. From the initial blast of the diagnosis, to the waves that may never settle to this day. There's always something to learn about me. Things to figure out how to get around, and new ways of thinking about myself and how I treat myself.

Some days my brain can be spicy, other days there's some other challenge to worry about. It's all about how I choose to conquer and move on from these daily challenges, even though they will change daily. Some days I will struggle, some days I will be winning. But it's important to always try.

It changes you

by Mary O' Sullivan-Fawcett

It changes you, illness
It changes how people treat you
Those that know you, love you, can't see the changes
Or don't want to, can't accept the new reality
New people only ever see the illness
They see it straight away, even hidden illness
It's in your eyes, your voice, your movement

It changes you, medication
Yes it eases your symptoms, your pain
But along with that come side effects
Added things to cope with
You need it though, it helps you through the day
Others don't realise that though
They just think you've changed, again

It changes everything, this thing inhabiting your body
In a heartbeat it's all over
Life as you know it is gone
And with that your dreams, hopes for the future
In its place comes fear, dread, hopelessness
Everything you didn't want for you
Or for them, those you love

My condition
by Gift

All that has affected my life? My condition. My legs are always paining, my back. So sometimes I cry because if I think long back ago things which I do by myself now I can't do it by myself. So it makes me stressed sometimes.

I stay alone. I stay alone. Sometimes I feel lonely because I stay alone. Except I go to church but my church is very far. It's in London. So to go there... sometimes once, after two months or three months.

Because of my condition, I can't stay in the bath for a very long time. My legs get swollen like this one. I have problem of wearing shoes because of my leg and I cannot walk a long distance.

So those things was too much for me. And the thing that was too much for me. I tried to apply for a bus pass but they would not give me. If I want to go anywhere I should pay but it's limited me for going out because of my condition. I can't walk long distance.

Those things affected me a lot in my life.

Sometimes I feel like "Let's go somewhere." For the sunshine or to the park. But I can't go there. But if I got a free bus pass, I can go.

Those things have troubled me. When I stay alone in the house, I think too much. I think of my children because I haven't seen them since 2006. I left my daughter when she was nine years now she is twenty four years. Without seeing her.

So those things when I'm staying alone in the house they come in my mind.

Isabel Marafao with a portrait of herself by Dr Larry Gurney

I am here, I am loved

by Isabel Marafao

In the beginning 30 years ago when I was diagnosed HIV positive the medication was so strong. I had 15 tablets a day, before lunch after lunch, before I go to bed I need to have 15. My diabetes didn't like that. Then I start every day with meds for HIV, the diabetes fight that a lot.

It caused some comas because of the stomach and the level of sugar. The fighting is always between Diabetes and HIV. Diabetes is a nightmare, HIV is a relief. Because with the medication we've got now I am stabilising and my CD4 count is always up 900. So I am okay with HIV.

All those things have made me what I am today, life is good but we need to manage, very well balanced. When I'm down I search for help, to speak to get advice.

30 years ago I went to my president at the tourism office, I told him I was HIV positive but that I still wanted to go on with my dreams. He said to me when you are getting problems you just tell me, but you can keep coming to work. I loved work, I loved coming to work.

My family was always with me, always accepting of me. The friends who don't accept me, I cut them out, because they don't understand me. I love what makes me live, it's the understanding , the connection between people. I spoke with people all around the world for my job, knowledge and acceptance makes me happy.

Life is to sort problems, every day, we need to keep going. Always with strength. For my well-being, I need to think more about myself. I'm trying to practice every day. To be present.I need to be more kind to me, sometimes I forget myself. My relationship with my disease is very good, since the support that England has given me since 6 years ago. I came here for the first time and the NHS saved me. I don't have a bowel. I was so bad, my daughter thought I was going away for forever. She asked me "what do you want me to do for you"..I want to be cremated or use my remains to grow a tree. She said "Okay mama".

Mother

by Liz Parkinson

I swim in the waters of my mother's life.

A river cold, dark and deep

with fear of sinking of being dragged into the dark.

My mother wailed and raged but I clung on.

Always kept my head above the water.

My mother wailed and raged and

I swam in her grief.

Effects

by Sarah Gunn

The effects on mental health

It effects my life

Because I am grieving

And have anxiety

I don't like crowds

Lots of people.

It effects sleeping

Effects breathing

It does effect other people

Family that must support my mental health

Grieving

Low feeling

Happy adventures

by Mark Barham

HIV has had a big ripple effect on my life. I didn't expect it to bring the most wonderful people in my life that wouldn't be there if it was not for HIV.

The fabulous people that work in all the HIV support groups, all the great clients. I have made some lifelong friends through this terrible disease. Through these great organisations I have been to Buckingham Palace. We (TVPS) were awarded The Queens award for voluntary services in 2013.

It was a day I will never forget. I hired a top hat and tails , so I looked very smart. I went with chairman, a volunteer and staff member. We got to see the royal family; My favourite was HRH Prince William.

The ripple effect has not always been positive though, through having side effects from the tablets I have had to pick jobs which would make it easier for me. I have been fired for having HIV and I have lost a business through HIV. It has all been about stigma really, People not understanding the illness.

It has affected past relationships and dating. I have had to have the dreaded talk about explaining I have HIV to partners. I am lucky enough that my partners have all been ok. It's really hard to have that discussion however, as you don't know how they will react.

I have witnessed first hand the stigma surrounding dating apps as well, even surprising the attitudes from gay men themselves. To this day HIV is still being stigmatised. I don't put my status on the apps anymore, I just have the discussion before I meet people, most people block or stop texting. You get used to it.

However the biggest effect it has had on me, I think it has made me more confident.

Just when you thought it was safe to get back in the water

by Steve Wood

Ofcourse, it's not all about sadness
I don't spend my days gazing at the navel of my madness
Life will go on, despite my petty storms
And my rebellious brain will continue to redefine my norms

At 5am on a workaday Thursday
I'm trying to find rhymes for this word and that
'Cos since Mr. Parkinson came to stay
Revealing himself as a grumpy old twat
It would seem he's awoken a sleeping beast
He is the hot water to my poetic yeast
Ironic, no, that the very thing
That left me feeling I was drowning
Should also make my senses sing
A torrent of expression so profound
It creates a pull, it brings me round
To wakening at 5am, too early even for light to peek out from under the covers
But just the right time to find a great rhyme to go with poetry lovers

Coping

How do we cope? Are we coping well?

"I have to be kind to me. I have to be good to me."

Take a look around

by Elvina Lee

As I sat in one of my favourite places in the Countryside. I took in the blue rich rippling lake, enjoyed the smell of nature, and felt comforted by the huge trees that surrounded me.

I felt the sun on my neck and felt alive.

I was grateful to be here.
I felt blessed to be here.

Today I wanted to take time out for me.
Yesterday I felt burdened by my diseases.

I am trying to learn to cope with my future and my present.

Whilst sat on this antique pine bench, I had to remind myself that I need to be patient with me.

I have to be kind to me.
I have to be good to me.

Do something I enjoy, practise self-care , keep praying, and be intentional with my journaling again, which includes my gratitude one too. Life has its ups and downs, twists, and turns.

I cannot change my medical history. But I know, no matter how tough it is, I know that I won't give up.

We're alright

by David Black

It's only one life as far as we know, so do we take it fast or slow?
The mind is such a powerful thing, it controls all we do, everything.
To cope you need to start with an attitude that supports you.
No matter what your health condition does to you.

To care is to take up a vocation, whether it's a friend or relation.
I care because it's what I must do. It's the right thing for me to do.
It's never really got me down, I'm a survivor in this town.
What does not beat me will make me stronger.

Diagnosing what is wrong, it can be short, it can be long.
Having a name to call it, it can help.
To define a destiny for your long-term health.
Don't over analyze as it won't help.

It's got easy to cope as time has gone by.
Acceptance of your fate, preparing for goodbye.
Living each day as it comes.
Enjoying the everyday in the rain and the sun.

I booked a hotel room on Monday

by Zoe Robinson

I booked a hotel room on Monday. I wanted a break from normal life, just one night. I wanted to press pause, put the world on a naughty step.

For one night, I pretended I had no responsibilities. I was not a disabled single mother of a disabled child, living on benefits, living under a death threat, living in Austerity Britain, Brexit Britain, Covid Britain.
For one night, I was not surrounded by dirty dishes, unanswered correspondence, my unpublished plays.
I booked a hotel room on Monday: clean sheets, unwrinkled; fresh bathroom, unstained; my own little kingdom, uncluttered. It was the closest I could get to an emergency bed on a psych ward. Look at me – putting 'hospital' into 'hospitality'!

In the mountains between France and Spain, near the tiny kingdom of Andorra, there is a village called 'L'Hospitalet'. In winter, the slopes of the Pyrenees are like white bed sheets. You can die in the mountains.
I booked a hotel room on Monday. My mental illness sneaked into my rucksack and came to the hotel with me.

HIV, mental health and lockdown

by Pauline Hass

I try to look on the bright side. I try not to let HIV get me down too much. There is nothing I can do about it. I have learnt to deal with it and coping with it.

Recently I started with menopause as well and that is taking a beating at the moment, as I don't sleep well because of night sweats. It's horrible. Some days my emotions are all over the place. Other days I am ok.

I decided not to go on HRT medication. I tried the herbal route, didn't help. I just take each day as it comes. I can deal with the fatigue, night sweats. What I can't sometimes deal with is the emotional roller coaster that I am currently on at the moment. But I deal with it as best that I can. I have my husband, Jorn that I can lean on and I can also talk to my best friend, Cheryl and lately I have made friends with my next door neighbour, Lorraine, who I can also chat to, which I am very grateful for. I did tell my oldest sister, Judith and my daughter, Tanya that I am in menopause. They are both still in South Africa. Judith understands, because she went through it. I really don't think Tanya really understands the whole menopause symtom. But It's up to her to do research herself.

Sometimes when I need my own space, I take walks to the park and around the horse stables where I am staying or just take a 20 minute bus ride into Whitley Bay. Pop off to the coffee shop and walk along the beach. I often do this on bright sunny days. I also read a lot. I knit for my 2 grandchildrenfrom my son and his partner that are staying in the UK. Some Fridays and weekends I baby sit, which I just love. Baby sitting just releases all the stress.

I think that I have come to the conclusion that I have to live with menopause until one day it just magically disappears.

My angel

by Mark Barham

Living with HIV is unique to us. We learn how to change our lifestyle and adapt to life with tablets etc.

My way of coping is I like to try and keep myself busy so I'm not thinking about it. I enjoy keeping busy at the HIV support group. It's great to see my friends and I always look forward to seeing them.

I am about to have my volunteer interview so I can do more at the centre, also I want to start doing talks to schools and doctors and nurses. It's my way of giving back and in a way, it helps talking about HIV and I can talk about myself for ages. Away from the centre I am trying to keep a small business afloat and live a life as full as I can. I don't talk about it to my family, so I am glad to have great amazing friends.

I only ever think about HIV properly is when I remember to take my 1 tablet a day. I have to remember to take it as I don't want to come immune to the tablets, as I have with my previous tablets. My bloods are only taken every 6 months now so I only have to think about that twice a year.

I was diagnosed a year after my sister was murdered. I suppose I didn't think much about it because my mind was still greatly based towards her. I left work as I was a real mess. It's really weird HIV. It didn't bring the family closer unfortunately. I was fortunate to have some amazing friends around me which helped with my diagnosis.

The day I lost you, my world collapsed
So many memories those were the facts
Your face every morning I will always remember
From January, June, August, and November
Your beauty, your smile was never false
To me you definitively had no faults
My heart will never fill again so brightly
I wish I could hold you tightly
Your picture greets me everyday
The lounge it sits, the joy it brings in every way
I will never forget you, fly with the angels
My sister, My life, My Angel

I only have one family member near me now and try to go and see them at least once a week.

I keep my toolkit close at hand

by NS

I cope – but it's a question of degree.
I keep the solution in my toolkit.
Yesterday I coped by cleaning the house,
Today I coped by seeing friends.
Tomorrow I will cope by going for a walk.
The day after I may feel slightly better – or slightly worse.
But I will definitely cope to some extent.

I have a wide variety of tools –
A mop and bucket to cleanse my surroundings,
Cooking utensils to make a meal to nurture my body,
A chat with my sister to give voice to my concerns,
A walk with a friend to release endorphins.

I keep them in my toolkit of self-care.
I do it because I am worth it.
I know one day soon I will recover the spring in my step,
And be ready to take on the world again.

Understanding and Accepting

by Maxine Patterson

"Are you coping?" An innocent sounding question, that threatens my equanimity; because of course coping implies

managing, being ok, carrying on with everyday life.

With Neuroendocrine Cancer every day is a lottery. What part of my insides will misbehave? Will I manage a full day away? Can I manage to go shopping? Can I cope with cleaning the house, or getting out into the garden to start preparing for the winter?

Being determined to "carry on" I always decide I can cope! And I do. I go shopping, I do the garden and then I'm surprised and angry when I'm flattened at the end of a few hours. Will power only get you so far. Feeling angry and annoyed with myself for not functioning in the way that I want to, makes me feel unhappy; because it's a reminder that I'm not coping, or at least not as well as I would like to.

Coping is also understanding and accepting what's happening to your body. Coping is getting the Doctors to accept that Neuroendocrine Cancer is a thing, a thing that affects the way your body absorbs nutrients and that you need extra strong vitamin D and Vitamin B – ordinary things – but it's exhausting how long it takes to work a way through the systems to get these essentials prescribed.

Coping is doing your hair, painting a face on. You're not pale and washed out looking, there are defined eyes and eyebrows. And yes; the wrinkles are still there, but hey!

Coping is accepting that you won't sleep. And if you actually manage five solid hours. That's a wow!

And accepting all those helpful hints that everyone feels bound to give you. Even though you know they don't work and never have worked!

And importantly, humour vital to help me and my partner get through some undignified times. Equally important is the ability to accept defeat and cry, scream and yell. Let out the pent up frustration and anxiety and then move on: all part of coping.

Nick Hargreaves with his favourite CD

Managing my mental health
by Nick Hargreaves

I cope pretty well with my mental health condition.

I know my own limitations, which I think is a good strategy for want of a better word to have because it's my way of putting everything into perspective.

After my bipolar diagnosis I coped pretty well but I made a lot of mistakes.

Now I cope a lot better as I'm used to my condition.

As far as coping methods go, I listen to a lot of nice music, exercise, walks, jogs, tennis.

And I involve myself in society a lot more than I used to.

It all helps.

Coping with my diagnosis

by Elaine

My Optician gave me my diagnosis and told me that I could have permanent sight loss unless I received immediate hospital treatment for macular degeneration which was now "wet". I was to "leave it with him" and "the hospital would be in touch".

I was alone. I live alone. I felt very much alone and frightened. This was a situation that my independent life experience could not fix. I was completely in the hands of faceless "others". I have no control.

Questions, so many questions.

How long do I wait?
Who will get in touch?
Which hospital?
What is the treatment?
Will the treatment work is this "thing" going to go away?
How do I live if it doesn't go away?
Can I live on my own?
Who will cook?
Who will clean and do the garden?
How will I cope?

This "thing" makes me feel so alone. It reminds me all the time of my limitations. I have difficulty doing things that I have done automatically for as long as I can remember. I can't read ordinary print. I can't drive. I can't read the cooker or washing machine dials. I can't do my hobbies. I can't do anything that involves detailed "looking". It drags me down just by the sheer constant reminders of what I cannot do and what I cannot see. My brain and body are still good – it's only my eyes that don't work properly.

I cry sometimes just out of sheer frustration with this "thing". Medication helps to flatten the ups and downs...but this "thing" never goes away. I try hard to be positive. I try hard not to "bother" anyone. I am stoical. I am often advised to "Be positive – instead of thinking about what you can't do, try thinking about what you can do". Really? I accept the advice is given with the best of intentions but please, let me be. Let me be my new unseeing self, in my own way. Let me carry on moving forward, discovering new things to do and doing what I can do but "better" and without limitations, just as I always did.

I know what I could do in the past, I know what I can do now. Please just ask me what I "want" to do and if I need help to do that "thing".

Coping not coping

by Dr Larry Gurney

I used to cope much easier. Coping was fighting against the virus, now there is never anything to fights, it was easier to fight the virus as a coping mechanism. Now the fight is most often against people - not worth bothering with and unlikely to succeed so I cope badly.

Similar to no.1 fighting, although I did not think I'd be still fighting after 20 plus years. I've retired from fighting against HIV for 10 years. By publicly exposing myself for the use of others I felt a duty, but these were different times. When I was alone I would often weep and on two occasions I "climbed the wall" not sure how I would get over the wall and escape

The tool I would like to have is a letter or a little card I would carry that would say "handle with care" I know I suffer from PTSD and fear especially of authority more especially dr's and health workers. I see them as the enemy who seem often to have no responsibility towards my mental health. Health care phobia. No more than that, they have the power of control over life or death and they know it!

If I held a card to explain this, I think it would be less easy for them to show disrespect or to respect my dignity. The only tools I use are the dogs they keep me alive. And painting can lift me. The sun too!

Are you coping? I'm existing not really giving back anything. Coping for me is about making a contribution. I don't think I'll ever be able to do that anymore. I'll never be 'remembered' which I think I wanted. Such is life!

Treatment

Exploring how we treat our health conditions.

"I'll be honest, I love my medication."

Tablets

by Mark Barham

Twenty seven to one.

I'm in Oldchurch hospital in Romford, Essex. It's 1997 and I've just been told I was HIV positive.
My friend Eve is with me and while I am a little shocked, I was kind of expecting it.
I'd had a one night stand 3 months before and the guy told me the following morning he had full blown Aids.

I asked the doctor what they could do to help me with the disease. He informed me that I was lucky, so much to say the anti-retriviral medication was available.
However I didn't realise how many tablets I would be taking. It started with quadruple therapy. I will try and remember them.

AZT, a white and blue capsule.
DDI, a large white chalky tablet.
Abacavir, a yellow tablet if I remember correctly.
Afarenze, not the correct spelling.

Anti diarroeah tablets, 2 tablets 4 times a day.
anti sickness tablets, 2 tablets 3 times a day.
Vitamins.
Paracetamol tablets.

I needed 2 tablet dispensers to house all these tablets, I really did rattle.
I hated taking the DDI as they were very big and I had to break them up and drink them with apple juice, both of which I hated.

I can remember taking the afavarenze in the morning and because I was working, I would become very high and it would feel like I was floating on the ceiling. I could of sold them as a drug.
Due to taking all these meds I needed to take anti diarreoh tablets to stop the inevitable happening. I can remember being in a busy shopping mall and after an accident, it was really embarrassing.

headaches were common place and also feeling sick.
The doctor informed me that there would be side effects however I didn't realise how many I would get. He asked me to photograph any visable ones. The weirdest one I can remember was a head to foot rash.

The advancement over the years has been amazing.
Though I became immune to a fair few tablets because I stopped taking them due to the side affects. My options were getting more and more limited. It got to a point where I was becoming to the end of options. I started taking kaletra and eventually onto my most recent tablet Trimeq.

I say tablet because I am now on one tablet, I get no side affects and I have been undetectable for seven years. I have now been HIV for twenty-five years.

Eight years

by Sarah Gunn

I have been on medication for about eight years

In the nineties I used to take herbal medication

　　for anxiety for social situations

Eight years ago I got depression with a higher active thyroid gland.

I was on tablets to balance things out to get my thyroid level right.

I'm also on antidepressants and vitamin tablets for iron levels.

I was put on tablets for anxiety and depression

　　by my GP at the doctor's surgery.

To help, I joined a walking group and did zumba classes.

After my mum died 2 years ago I kept busy

　　doing arts crafts and textiles at home.

Recently I lost my partner.

I have strategies to cope.

I do mindfulness exercises at home.

I had a phone call from my doctor yesterday.

I have to go back on my thyroid medication because my levels were high.

I am still take antidepressants and vitamin tablets to help my conditions.

Pop pop

by Liz Parkinson

I'll be honest, I love my medication. It works.

It keeps me calm, it keeps the darkness at bay.

Medication and the ability of taking care of myself.

Every morning I pop my pills. Pop, pop. I'm grateful the day begins.

Busy, busy, I keep myself busy.

I'm here, I'm there.

I surround myself with friends with people talk, talk.

I'll be honest I love my medication pop, pop the pills everyday.

It works and I'm mostly happy, I'm ok and I'm grateful.

Maintaining my equilibrium

by NS

I take the medication because it works for me. Simple as that.

It enables me be the authentic version of myself – to thrive -

To leave behind the soreness and shrug off the anxiety.

So, I open my mouth and in they go.

Those tablets and me, we're made for each other.

Without them I would be twisted in pain and sucked down by anxiety.

And my life would be limited by an unfilled prescription.

So, opening the box and swallowing those pills hands me back my life.

It's part of who I am.

My Medication

by Mary O'Sullivan-Fawcett

'I won't even take an aspirin.'
How often do people say that?
I think I'm supposed to feel they're brave
Or that I'm a total wimp, or some kind of addict

My reply is this
You have not been in enough pain, mental or physical
Or unable to cope with whatever life has thrown your way
Simply put, maybe one day you'll understand

I would never wish anything bad on those people
I just wish they would stop being so sanctimonious.
Try listening to those of us who need help
And stop judging me

I take two injections a week
That's another one,
'I could never put a needle into myself'
My answer
if you needed to, you would, believe me
Those two injections, without them I wouldn't move at all

I take in excess of thirty pills a day
Some ease my mind & keep me halfway sane
Others dumb down my pain so that I can function like a 'normal' human
Whatever that means

Honestly?
None of them totally take away my pain.
It eats at me every moment of every day
But without them
I dread to think

Oh the walking stick is not for fun, it keeps my upright, helps me walk
And stops me from falling flat on my face, most of the time.

Victoria Gray

Medication

by Victoria Gray

Medication. I don't mind it, if I pretend it's a smartie I can even swallow it without water.
A while ago I was told I shouldn't be taking so much, I must admit I did feel a bit beyond my years going to boots to buy a pill box.

So I cut down and my chest felt tight for a few weeks but then I adapted and we kept moving on. My pill box became less like a maraca.

I have tried a few routes to feel less depressed, venturing among the 'ines' (If you get it you get it) but they made me want to end my life, funnily enough increasing how many I took did not help.
So I went back to the one I started on and felt relief. Now I am smiling again.

I also take craving pills for alcohol. But I'm not an alcoholic anymore.
That was a long time ago now but the results of the pills work best when you take them consistently for a year, so into my pill box they go. They are my most smartie like pill.

My heart is a bit too fast at times. So I pop a pink pill into my mouth when it starts to affect my mind. This slows it down a bit and means I find it easier to do things like go outside, get on buses, speak to people and enjoy myself.

I used to not be able to do buses. But now I can.

Continence Care Products

by Barry Wilkinson

I wore a kind of rubber mask over my penis.

Not for fun, but because I couldn't hold urine. It had a long nozzle like tube that ran into a urine collection bag attached to my leg. The whole thing was made of rubber and looked like a Second World War pilots gas mask. It would sometimes suction onto my penis, swelling it up but not in a good way. It either stank of pee or the bleach my Mam washed it in.

When plastics came along they were a god send. Easy to use, breathable, light and single use. Now I felt clean and fresh most of the time. There was a huge variety. There is a product called a 'conveen'. Think condom with a nozzle. For this product to work well you have to measure the length and girth of your penis. This can be terribly disappointing when you're 13.

From the age of 15 I had a surgical opening created on my stomach. Called a stoma it was created using some small bowel. I hated it. A strawberry red blob on my belly resembling some kind of Star Trek alien. It needed bags that were sealed around it. There is a convenience to bags of course. You rarely get caught short, you can pee almost anywhere and they hold quite a lot. But be careful! One time, when away with friends I got very drunk and fell asleep without emptying my bag. My friends noticed how full my bag was and proceeded to drag me to the toilet over every wooden raised doorstep. Bruised and battered, the next morning I asked 'why didn't they just use a bucket?'

Most of my life has been an attempt to move away from the urine bag, and now I am there! I now have a bladder that holds urine and I don't use a bag, I use a urinary catheter. A long thin tube that slides up the penis into the bladder. I like to get it out in front of burly men and describe how I push it up there. Built to make even the manliest of many men pale into insignificance. It is for that reason that I rarely use a urinal. I can't have lines of men collapsing around me. I always use a cubicle for privacy and hygiene reasons. This can often entail a long wait. I have occasionally used a disability toilet, but because my issues are not visible I feel guilty. Should I take out my catheter on entry, brandishing it in order to prove my credentials. Maybe not. Still, things have come a long way since the Second World War pilots mask

Trick or treat

by Tony Moore

Why they call it "treatment" I do not know. There is no "treat" involved!
Indeed, there is no "treat" meant!

There is no "treat" in taking medication to numb the pain and deal
    with stress and anxiety which leaves you drowsy the next morning.
There is no "treat", especially when you have a fear of needles
    in injecting yourself with insulin 4 times a day
    and pricking your finger to read your blood sugars.
There is no "treat" in having to regularly dress even the smallest
    of wounds in your lower legs for fear of serious infection.
There is no "treat" in taking antibiotics that make you sick,
    bung you up or that give you diarrhoea!
There is no "treat" in having to use a walker to get about.
There is no "treat" in needing to use support
    to sit down and raise to use the toilet.
There is no "treat" in not being able to put normal socks on
    but having to struggle even more to put "compression socks" on.

I could go on. I receive a lot of "treatment" without the "treats"
My reward, if not a "treat" is that thanks to the NHS, for which I am eternally
grateful. I have these facilities at my disposal and my life is richer for this.

No gain without pain!

Treatment

by David Oliver

Where to begin. I guess a large dose of medication would suffice. A lot of a little pill called Fluoxetine. Some Beta Blockers for the anxiety symptoms and the latter makes that a lot worse.

How do you treat something that has no real cause? Just a brain imbalance and one of the many spicy delights of Autism. A constant struggle to find medication that works, and a therapist who is willing to listen. Obviously being around people helps. There's ups and downs. Sometimes Extreme, and sometimes gradual. It's difficult to pinpoint when it's happening. I know when it's okay, and eventually pickup when it gets bad. But that's the thing. It's a lifelong battle. Not something that can be cured. The ethics of 'Curing' Autism and their co morbid conditions is a complex and difficult ethical nightmare. Some people want to fix us. Make us fit in. To adhere to the standards of a world not made for us.

And often barely manageable. I wish I could flick a switch and turn it off at will, but I can't. I will never be able to feel normal or fit in to other people's standards. People will often try and figure out what it's like in my shoes. To try and represent us and do more damage than good. Without the conversations. Training or even basic human decency.

It's important to remember that whatever our circumstances, conditions or issues. We are all human.

We have feelings, needs, desires. We long to be understood and helped. I speak for the thousands of us who have no voice. Who aren't heard or listened to. I'm trying to start those conversations.

But we can't do it without you.

Misconceptions

The stigma, stereotypes and presumptions that come with a diagnosis.

*"Would they do the same if I broke my leg
instead of my mind and heart?"*

Stigma
by Gift

They think we are helpless because of the stigma. And we are worthless.
I can't tell everybody. I'll tell some but I can't tell everybody.

What good can come from her?
Nothing good can come from her.

People need to be educated that to be HIV+ is not the end of the life.
I should keep my life as usual.

Nothing changed because I am HIV+
They say "if I have HIV now, I will sell sell my things because I'm going to die"
I will tell them you should keep on doing what you're doing.
If I did that. Where I would be now?
I'd be suffering.

You'll live as long as others

Misconceptions
by DK

I always thought that if I talked or didn't hide behind a mask and people saw the real me that people would see me as a stereotypical 'lunatic' you'd see on TV or something.

I'm scared of getting a diagnosis because people just think I'm eccentric or jokingly say I'm mentally deranged but if or when I get a label, so how will they react.

I wish people would realise I don't intend to cause hurt and it's not because I'm thoughtless, something I'm not in control and I don't know it.

People think when I used to cut it was because I was depressed or wanted to end it but that was never the case, it was nothing to do with that.

I wish you knew

by Victoria Gray

When I mention that I have OCD I usually get a joke like 'oh are you clean then?' or 'can you come clean my house?'. Behind a smile and laugh at the ignorance my mind flashes to the depth behind obsessive compulsive disorder. Wishing to transfer what I'm seeing to the minds of others, to the true raw horror. I wish it was just enjoying picking up an antibac bottle.

OCD preys on your morals and core values, seeking to work against them. Your mind stops being your own.

For example, I have a cat called Stormy. Stormy can sometimes be naughty. One time she was attacking my feet and I thought about how annoying she is. My mind moved on to how annoying she can be in general. I then thought about what could be a scenario where she would not have the power to be naughty.
My mind went to thinking about her in the sea.
My mind really vividly imagined it, I visualised her struggling to stay up, panicking in the water, getting swallowed by the waves up and coming back up with her eyes all big and scared.

So anyway...
OCD preys on your morals and core values. It played on my fear of animals dying, of my love for my cats, my fear of a loss of control. I still carry around the immense guilt and shame of having this thought, a thought I could not control, a thought that was not mine.

So no I don't want to clean your house, I can't keep my own house clean.

Mary Pickin

It hurts

by Mary Pickin

The trouble with Mary is
She goes on a bit
She goes on and on
She's always griping
She's boring
She can't control her drink
She ruins a good time
She's not fun anymore

The trouble with Mary is
She's a drama queen
She needs to calm down
She's an attention seeker
She wants us to feel guilty
She's no self confidence
She's far too serious
She's no fun anymore

I can't be bothered with her
Can you?
Let's not invite Mary
Don't tell her though
Just keep her in the dark
Keep shtum about it
It's her own fault really
She's just too much
She should seek professional help.

It hurts when you're mentally unwell
And your friends dont want to understand
It's your fault, you're weak
It's just self indulgence
Would they do the same if I broke my leg
Instead of my mind and heart?

Tomorrow

by AD

When I was in school, we usd to hear about it, they used to come to our schools, they would talk about it. I used to hear so many people cry about the situation, that there's no good medication for it. When I was in South Africa, many people died from HIV. There was awareness, people came to the schools to talk about it.

In my case when I was diagnosed, I thought my world had ended. There was no use living because I was definitely going to die from it. Then I started coming to BST and there was people who were living their life, they're healthy, they're taking their medication. Then I started feeling better, being lively again. Because I thought in a few years you just pass on, for four months I was so unhappy, taking care of so many things, how will my future be, what am I living for, how will I tell people I've been diagnosed.

When I was in a shared house they knew they were treating me like nothing, they thought because I was close to them I could infect them. The woman in the house said you have to tell everyone, you have to tell everyone. Within that there was stigma, they were taking me to be someone who could infect them because we cooked together, lived together. Even though I knew I could not infect them, so I left the house. They didn't care what I was going through. I'm happy that I left. I feel safe now, at least I'm not made to feel bad.

I haven't told anyone about my HIV, apart from BST and the hospital. Sometimes I feel like when I go to the hospital when I go to Ward 90, I'll see someone I know, what are you doing here, why are you here. When I go there I always pray I won't meet anyone that I know, I haven't told a close friend or my daughter. Nobody Knows.

To tell someone I'd need to be brave, to be confident in myself. To tell my daughter would be my first priority. I need to be confident, I need to prepare myself for it. The day I will say it, I won't care what they'll say about it.

People really don't know what we are facing, yes I'm positive and yes I'm going through a lot. But when I'm around people I put that aside and show my happy face to them, people do not want to know what you are going through. They should ask, are you okay, you don't look happy, I am listening. You don't know what this person is going through until you understand what they are thinking. So when it comes to the HIV aspect of it, you really need to listen, to learn. One day, just one day they may encounter what you are going through, you should put people's problems in front of you because tomorrow it could be their turn.

Misconceptions
by David Oliver

The truth is I had no idea going into this how deeply complex it would be. It's been a huge journey of discovery that may never end. It's not an on/off style switch. It's a series of sliders. Each day poses different challenges and learning curves. You won't always know what to do, or where you fit in. You won't always have a place to go in times where you just need a helping hand. You'll spend a lifetime second guessing yourself and telling yourself that you aren't good enough. You won't always be listened to. Taken seriously. There is no such thing as looking Autistic or looking depressed or anxious. If anything, it's getting spicier with age not better. No there is not an easy way to access services. Yes, every day will be different.

This is a lifelong condition that will never disappear. And it's up to me to start those conversations and fight for basic representation. We are not the cliché of the movies. We are so much more than a diagnosis. A piece of paper, or a stigma. We move past the ableism, and we survive.

Yes, we need more funding. More research, more understanding. But we also need your love and respect.

Never assume

by Mary O'Sullivan-Fawcett

I see you, looking at me
Walking so slow a tortoise will beat me
You maybe saw me pop a few pills
I really need them to live each day

You see a woman, wrong side of 50
Walking stick in hand
Hair a colour that clearly isn't natural
Docs on my feet

Shouldn't be doing that at my age

You see me slowly approach my car
Ungracefully get into it
Then you see the windows come down
The music go up, loud, and I'm off
Those wheels are my legs

I struggle every day
I sometimes just want to give up
Then I look in my box of tricks
I have tickets for the flicks, theatre and gigs
With my sister at my side I'll give most things a go

The next time you look at someone and assume
Think again, age is a number
Music and the arts transcend time, place and age

Just 'cos you're getting older doesn't mean
    you should stop doing what you enjoy
And guess what, this old bird has one of the hottest tickets
    in town Sam Fender at St. James' Park

Can't bloody wait.

Happy as

by Dr Larry Gurney

I had started volunteering at London lighthouse HIV centre before and when I returned to Uni I was elected education + welfare vice president of the union so had planned a campaign about HIV. So in theory!! I thought I pretty much knew everything then in the June just before taking up the post I seroconverted.

The shock was I had never never done anything sexual to get infected. So what the hell. I was horrified. I was confused. It made no sense.

It seems however there are strange things going on in advice on transmission. If you happen to have had cancer and your immune system is compromised and you have sex oral sex with a person who is only just infected you can get transmission for oral oral sex. But such rare events are too complicated to be mentioned in advisory leaflets. So just a bit of *bad luck.*

By far the worst stigma comes from 2 places the gay community and the NHS. Both should not be the case. Initially I fought against these 2 stigma hot spots – but now ive given up on both. You become "unclean" apparently and gay dating apps are full of the phrase "must be clean and STD free" cleans means you must not have HIV in most peoples heads. So now I have accepted it is not worth being part of the majority gay community so I will be alone. My fear with the NHS is going into Durham hospital who will one day likely cause me harm (as they have in the past) or they will simply euphonize me somehow.

Presumptions: the main one is the presumption I would die in 3 years as the experience in the early 90s was that violent seroconversers would rapidly develop into AIDS. Other presumptions are usually the result of ignorance like my first partner insisted on me not using a razor to shave so he bought me an electric shaver. Which I hated. He argued that microcuts would leave HIV blood on my face.

In Africa HIV is seen as a black disease so when I work and (illegible) people are shocked at my HIV status.

I'm sure there are 100's of presumptions I've faced and forgotten. 30+ years is a long time!

What is something I wish?

That I am a human, full of anxieties and troubles but also full of emotion and with a lot of love all this before an "AIDS."

I wish I could accept the above but sadly I can't. I am rather 'fucked up.'

I cannot believe this ' u = u' thing perhaps when it's true to others I will believe it.

U = u / undetectable is untransmutable.

I know that if I had not got involved in changing the medical outcomes back down in 90s medications would not be in our hand. So I should get involved in this u=u thing to teach and contribute to the change. But I am exhausted fighting for me and other people. Its easier to just face away from society, relationships and someone elses love. A sad sad situation really.

Presumptions

by Lynn

Presumptions. People think that you know all about HIV.

When I first got diagnosed I told my sister and a friend. I was late in my life, 50 years old. It was after my husband died. And you would have thought that by that age. I would know better and take precautions.

And when I told my family at a party, I just blurted it out. All my family was very sympathetic. Maybe I shouldn't have told people after having a drink.

Presumptions.
Everyone "knows" that... People in their ignorance think that if you have HIV it can become full blown AIDS. If you don't look after yourself and take the tablets that prevent you from developing full blown AIDS.

Literally speaking

by Tony Moore

I am Autistic. I interpret literally. Because of this people misconceive that I am stupid. They misconceive that I am slow. They misconceive that I am pedantic. This is the most damaging to me.

What I read, what I see is quite often different to what others read or see. Being Autistic means that I am also Neurodivergent. My brain is wired up differently. I picture most things, even written things.

Here are a few examples.

If I see a sign that says, "Wet Floor!" to me that is an instruction to wet the floor.
If I see a sign in a garment that says "Wash dark colours separately" I put each dark item of clothing in the washing machine on its own!
If I see a sign that says "Pedestrians. Do not walk on the road!" –my brain is confused. There is such a sign next to the pedestrian crossing in Newcastle's Eldon Square bus station. When I first saw this, I was left confused and did not know what to do.
If I see a job advert that says, "You need to hit the ground running!" I am equally confused. I picture myself with mobility issues and unable to walk very well, never mind running, taking a tumble and then trying to get up and run. It won't happen. It puts me off applying for jobs that I may otherwise be ideal for.
Similarly, if in a job interview, I am told that "We need to see how you think on your feet!" I assume that they want me to stand up to answer the question! If someone says to me "Are you alright?" my immediate response is that I am symmetrical, and as such I am half left! When I saw a sign in a washroom stating, "Please put all paper towels in the waste bin!", I took each and every paper towel out of the dispenser and put them in the bin.

Am I being misconceived? Am I misconceiving these instructions, or is everyone else?

One thing for sure is that if instructions were written in plain English and without any ambiguity, life would be simpler!

Would be a lot less fun though!

Pip McDonald

Me, Myself, My Knee and I

by Pip McDonald

I experienced a knee injury while playing football in London in 2018. I remember trying to explain that I was not able to run due to concerns about my knee injury and it felt like some people did not accept what I had said.

"Don't use your knee as an excuse" they said.

I don't know if they were right or not or whether they were trying to encourage me to run. Maybe I was being too cautious. Perhaps the misconception was my own. Ultimately, I was worried that if I ran again then I might damage my knee again and not be able to walk. I was able to run a few years later, not as fast as I was in the past, but this did not matter. The member of staff who shared my scan results said I could run. Others shared their perceptions and dismissed my injury and the impact it had. All I knew was that my right knee was not the same as my left knee and I could not straighten my right leg. Sometimes when I walk, I limp a bit, but the injury is largely 'invisible'. What happens when you cannot 'see' injuries and their impact on a person? Whilst I cannot play football anymore, I have been able to run and race in my own way accommodating the injury. I completed the Great North Run in 2021, various 10ks, and completed a 50-mile challenge in my backyard in isolation during the pandemic.

Do what you can with what you have got!

It's a Waiting Game

by Maxine Patterson

The fact that it took nearly ten years for my cancer to be diagnosed, underlines the major misconception about Neuroendocrine Cancer. Often patients are dismissed as being hysterical, mentally unstable, having IBS. And many, many patients echo this experience.

Thus, the major misconception about my health condition is with the Health Service in general.

I carry details of my Cancer on a card, which I share with any Doctor, nurse, dentist, or any other medical professional that I come into contact with; because without fail; they have no idea what it is! Frustrating beyond belief!

The symbol of Neuroendocrine Cancer is a zebra. Doctors in their training are taught to think about common causes for illness, "listen for the hoofbeats, think horses, not zebras." – Neuroendocrine Cancer UK and linked organisations across the world are urging Drs and medical professionals to think of other possibilities, think about zebras as well as horses.

But it's a long job and the average time for diagnosis is between six and seven years. By the time I was diagnosed I had seven tumours and my stomach was blocked; but the consultant insisted I had IBS! A very, very common story amongst NET patients.

When I was told that I had Neuroendocrine Cancer I was recovering from a biopsy. The endocrinologist hesitantly explained what it was. He had never had met an actual Neuroendocrine Cancer patient before!

I knew then that this was going to be tricky, I got out my little notebook and wrote everything down, asking about spellings and all the details. That part of my life is now second nature, everywhere I go that concerns doctors, dentists and other medical professionals I take my information and always, always make detailed notes. A paramedic in the ambulance, rushing me to hospital with a suspected heart attack, wanted to know all about Neuroendocrine Cancer. Telling him everything, helped keep me calm!

The Gendered Experience

How does our gender affect our experience?

*"The binary system is the thing, even gender
is given the code that guides care one way or another."*

Twins

by Zoe Robinson

My very best friend, Glenn, is so similar to me that I refer to him as my twin. He lives at the other end of the country, and during our nightly phone calls, we often discover that we coincidentally ate the same food that day, bought the same item or injured the same limb.

We also have the same phobias and neuroses, the same compulsions and emotional reactions, the same way of seeing the world and describing what we mean.

In our early 40s, we each received an important medical diagnosis.
'I'm Autistic, apparently,' Glenn told me.
'They've got it wrong!' I said. 'You're the same as me, and I've just been told I have Emotionally Unstable Personality Disorder.'

We dutifully settled into our assigned roles. Glenn took his new diagnostic label as carte blanche to withdraw from society. I, because of my responsibilities as a single mother, threw myself into every psychotherapy I could get my hands on.

In terms of the health system, our diagnoses meant that Glenn fell off the radar whereas I was stigmatised and traumatised. Here are some things that medics told me:
GP: You can't possibly have insert physical health condition. There's nothing wrong with your body. You're just attention-seeking.

A+E: Your test result is unusual, and we would normally repeat the test in half an hour, but you're a mental health patient, aren't you? So, we won't bother.

Consultant: A trained monkey could see that you have insert physical health condition. Why the hell weren't you referred to me before?

My physical health condition was finally diagnosed. Also, my Personality Disorder diagnosis was changed to Autism, which feels right, because Glenn and I are twins.

Objectivity Vs Subjectivity

by Dr Larry Gurney

Being a man is different to being a gay man. Is it? Yes I suppose so. I experienced a huge shift when I seroconverted, although at the time they did not know it was seroconversion. Having had cancer the year or so before I had a very different 'social' response to illness. The moment that I shifted to HIV, it felt like control was removed from me as if I had no right to very much at all.

An interesting contrasting experience began when I started international work. Firstly peoples pre conceptions of what a gay man changed under the spot light. It often said I dont appear 'gay' whatever that means, so as a white man in several African HIV settings, disclosing my HIV status was seen as somewhat shocking to the large and small groups i disclosed to whilst helping to fight the stigma, more importantly to women in trials, Women's immunology varies in many ways. The issues I was mostly interested was mother to child transmission and HIV in children. All of this was so important in my early work in Africa.

Men rarely, if ever, disclosed in Southern Africa. They were hidden and hiding and sadly continued to keep infecting women. I admit I rarely understood 'straight men'. My main obsession was to reduce the very rates of transmission to babies 85% or higher to those women on no transmission. We knew we could get this as low as 5%. Most women seem to take on a role as protector of the child and family. Because we had so little data on HIV, pregnancy we had no idea what HIV medication would have on the feus. Study showed that most viral shedding took place at the birthing- blood present ingested. It is hard when mostly men are letting women they (>) take medication, have C sections, do then do that. To be honest if it had not been for the brave women in S Africa just doing as they are 'told' HIV levels would still be staggering.

I suppose as a gay man, willing to talk womens issues, understanding the science and having greater empathy for women it was easier i was perhaps less threatening.

I'm sure my own HIV status helped, on several times I was accused of lying about my HIV status and on occasion took a lateral flow test in front of assembled groups to prove.

Infected

In the early days in the UK there were no women in the support groups so we discussed originallyin a sort of detached way. It was all about HIV and men-and not just men-It was a gay men or bi men-MSM-Many of whom did not say themselves at risk-getting straight me engaged was also very difficult. The only group often who self-identified were drug users or the hemophiliac group. Who at the same time really waited to have anything to do with us.They were victims. We were guilty and deserved it.

So I often blank blank? HIV in women's groups. In the US there were more women and the issuesI just found more interesting. The truth is this was mostly academic to me- to understand the difference in the immunology in women.I tended to approach HIV in this very academic way. It was easier. But then when eventually we had positions on community advisory groups CAB, I could at least question the big pharma companies about involving women in trials. Women's immunology varies in many ways. The issues I was mostly interested in was mother to child's transmission.

HIV is different in so many ways for women brackets in my opinion bracketsFirstly they are victims of transmission. The disgusting rates of rape in South Africa illustrate how negative paternal societies can be. Why? Why is sex so important? Men seeing it is their marital right often means women have little control. Alcohol isn't is endemic and many SA countriesand drink and sex consensual or rape go hand in hand.men are dangerous to many women. Men often do not get tested then therefore do not take medication and hence are always verile and capable of past transmitting again again.That sometimes seems to be no loyalty and men who are infected to protect If it was even rumored that if you pass it on you can use that as a cure. Likewise a certain myth of having sex with a virgin or even a baby. It is hard to know whether these myths came from.

One thing in early days worth mentioning are the rituals of manhood. Bush camps for young men can last a month or more. During this time men are taught to be a man! Ritual circumcision used traditional blades to cut each youth ina roll. HIV was often transmitted as the blade was shared. It took a lot of work to change traditional practices.

So sexuality and gender are a fascinating side of my own journey with HIV. It changes people's opinion and perspective of me as a person.It helps some ways to be less threatening to women allowing me to broaden my view of the HIV world. My early academic interestsWas driven by a need to knowbut also to get away from the gay man centered views. Then I went to Southern to the Southern Hemisphere the HIV world was the opposite of the global north it was a women's issue.

HIV is a glorious virus. It has found a perfect host not biologically perfect as a horseBut it exploits all the ridiculous nature of mankind. It's taboo; It's needs; its paternal rules; It is humans who have allowed HIV to control it by the nature of us as a ridiculous species. We have all the tools to stop it but sadly not the intelligence to act. It should be ca;;ed the humans stupidity virus. Sex, gender, rape, rites, rights, war, violence, alcohol. drugs, power, control, loneliness, needs, lack of communication, lack of opinions, fears and silence.

I have tried to break these taboos but more just pop up over and over again. So much so that now I don't think I have the energy anymore to fight for anyone. Stigma keeps the ignorance fertile and we cannot win. Women shall keep losing the power of control, men still keep causing wars and use rape as a weapon; men keep taking power and moreof backwards why why do we allow it to keep happening apathy I suppose. Sadly I could I also have apathy after 30 years of fighting I really cannot be bothered anymore! New paragraph

I have seen decades of pain from the 1980s onwards, Eventually the capacity to be part of the human race ebbs away.

Violet Rook

Gender and Algorithms

by Violet Rook

Algorithms and pathways affect our lives,
Everything is assigned to a pattern of numbers 1 and 0.
The binary system is the thing,
Even gender is given the code that guides care one way or another.
The individual is anonymous, yet be it cancer care or arthritis,
The algorithms design our fate.
And influence the treatment we are given.
Youth and age are part of the story.
For whoever writes these magic programmes
decides the pathway our lives will take.
They also influence what professionals think.
An athlete can have problems with bones and joints,
        an older person is just an arthritic.
Do they see the person or is it cost and effect that reigns supreme.
The algorithms hide behind a system with an image of care,
But is that fair.
We are all individuals surely that is the factor which should be seen, and
Knowledge of those caring the deciding factor in the pattern of life.

Living with albinism

by Liz Gregson

Men and women share many common experiences living with albinism and the associated eye condition. However, there have been times when my experiences being a girl/woman with albinism has been different. When I was a child walking along a street people sometimes shouted "Albino" at me. This made me uncomfortable, particularly as I didn't really understand the meaning of the word at that age. Would this have happened if I was a boy?

As an adult I sometimes had unsettling experiences, which I attributed to appearing distinctive with limited eyesight. I will mention 2 separate incidents, including a time when 2 boys cycled past me and grabbed my hat. I felt shaken and couldn't see where they had gone, but was grateful when one of the boys cycled back to give me my hat.

An alarming incident happened while I was reading on a train late in the evening when I felt I was being watched. The man was sitting on the other side of the carriage, then he quickly moved to sit opposite me and snatched my paper out of my hand. I told him to go away and he mumbled "Too close" then continued staring at me. He appeared intimidating and I felt frightened and concerned for my safety. Would that have happened to anyone with good eyesight or to a man?

When I was pregnant I looked forward to having my regular scan and hoped to see my growing baby. I felt disappointed when I was unable to see the images on the monitor, which was situated too far away, and couldn't be moved closer. Although I was relieved when I was assured everything was normal I felt robbed of the opportunities to see my developing baby and left feeling deflated. In contrast, my husband was thrilled to be able to see our baby. I asked for a hard copy of photos, but they weren't available at that time, so I missed out on that valuable experience.

As I've grown older people no longer shout at me in the street, possibly because my platinum blonde hair colour isn't unusual for people in their 60s. However, I have sometimes been subjected to harsh comments from people when I have been unable to see something, particularly when shopping. At times their lack of understanding or sensitivity makes me feel upset and angry. Would this have happened if I was a man?

Unfortunately, people sometimes don't understand what life is like for people living with different eye conditions, which can lead to them being intolerant. In my experience I feel this more evidently having albinism and being female.

Friends are everything

by Mark Burham

I can remember when I was younger and trying to research about HIV, there was much more information relating to gay men but hardly anything based towards woman. I think back in the early days HIV was known as the gay disease only caught by gay men. Back then Aids was not called that , it was called GRID which stood for gay related immune deficiency. If there had been more information available to woman I think the statistics would have been a higher proportion to the known figures at the time, because of this woman were at a higher risk in my opinion.

I think this had a considerable influence on how sexuality was translated by men and women in the community. More leaflets were available about high risk activity including anal sex.

I think I am perceived more as a gay man with HIV more than if I had been a woman. As it was more prevalent. Also that I caught it through a one night stand, not that ladies don't have them, just that I think people would be intrigued how I caught it if I had been a straight woman, for instance.

I have a straight female friend who I have known for about 15 years. She told me this, "I think my sex definitely made a difference of not being diagnosed sooner. I had all the symptoms recognisable with HIV/AIDS and do believe that had I been male or a gay man that it would have been suggested to me to take a test for it. A gay young friend told me years ago , that any time he had to go to the doctor's, they suggested he do a test for HIV. I didn't seem to fit a 'category' it wasn't expected of me/people like me?"

When I used to do school talks to students, I would get more questions asked by girls than boys. I think that was because women look after their health better, men are the last people to go to the doctors if they have a problem. Guys are more embarrassed.

We have got better over the years and the rates of mother to baby transmission rates have fallen due to the fact of the medications and early testing. A child would not normally live past their 2nd birthday without proper hiv medication. That's why it is such an issue in African societies.

This has been quite noticeable for me as I have gone round the country attending HIV support groups. There are normally more ladies that go than men, which I am surprised about, I suppose not really when men are less likely to get tested.

The biggest problem around today is the people who don't know they have the virus. There are married men on the cruising scene who have sex with men and then go home to their wives. How many of these women are unaccounted for?.

If more people were open to getting HIV tests , we would have better figures on how many people have HIV. Because it is so much better to get diagnosed early and get the treatment available than not to.

I choose female

by Jean Angus

My first two consultants were men. To them, I was unusual, somebody to study and bring the medical students in to learn. A rare condition indeed. "Can we show you, expose you in the pursuit of medical knowledge".

Later, I was under a different consultant, and a female SpR. Strangely we'd come across each other at the gym but didn't know each other. We acknowledged each other and I explained, as I had with the men, that I felt self- conscious when I swam and yet that was the exercise I most enjoyed. That was the reason that I hoped to find medication or treatment which would reduce the look and feel of my skin.

Empathy in her eyes. Two women who understood the fear of scrutiny, comparison and gossip and how it can grind you down if you let it in.

The NHS

Sharing experiences of the National Health Service

*"I'm still alive after 51 years so that
has to be a good thing right?"*

Why?

by Dr Larry Gurney

Oh my god. I could write a book, a thriller or a horror.
    I live in *fear* of ever having to use Durham Hospital.
I would rather if sick get on the X1 to get to the RVI in Newcastle.
I can't write about it really, it upsets me too much.
But then the RVI is safe.
I've been chopped, cut out, abused and feel as if
    I've been *violated* so many times.
Perhaps I feel safer in London Hospitals.
It's a story of two tales. One appalling and the other one good.
Poole Hospital is loving and allows *dignity*,
Chelsea and Westminster Hospital is good.
Royal Marsden Cancer centre was good.

The problem is I expect to have *dignity* but I live near a place
    that I know will one day kill me.
Why is it so different?
Each year a new addition to this list of potential death threats
    adds to my fear of Durham Hospital.
The last time they would have killed me
    if I had not *screamed* to contact the RVI.
Please someone take away the *fear*.
DIGNITY DENIAL.
Why should we accept such differences?

The Needle, The Archetype and The Volunteers

by Pip McDonald

When I received my second COVID vaccine

I was really struck by the staff

They recognised that I was nervous about the needle

and tried to distract me

They did not have to do that

But chose to help

I was very thankful for their kindness

They worked extremely long hours

And did not have to help

The majority of staff were volunteers

Working very long hours

which was incredible

Needles seem counterintuitive

Like an archetype that can pose a primal threat

Their kindness dissolved that fear

Kindness could be a new universal archetype

Thank you

Pauline Hass

No complaints

by Pauline Hass

When I first arrived in the UK at end October 2019. My husband helped to register with the Dr's and RVI hospital, as he came a few months before me.

My consultant who I met for the first time at RVI, did all the legwork, and I still currently deal with her. Dr Jill is so awesome. I have absolutely no complaints about her. She explained what a consultant is and what it all entails. The terminology in South Africa is totally different to the UK, especially in the medical field and can be very confusing. But I am getting used to it.

Medication that I was taking in South Africa is different to UK and the RVI doesn't supply that medicine, so my medication had to be changed. The Dr mentioned that the medicine that I was taking in South Africa might have done some kidney damage, which the Dr is still trying to sort out for me.

I also met with a lady called, Christine. She was a human rights person. Can't remember her full title. I had a few counselling sessions with her. Unfortunately she is no longer working in the same department. She was also very awesome, and I have absolutely no complaints. I also met with a specialist HIV nurse at RVI. The nurse, Nicola, takes my bloods every time I have an appointment. The receptionist, Fiona, at RVI. All these people are all awesome. They all put me on the right track. No complaints at all.

The only thing at the moment that I am not happy with, is the way that things are run at the local Dr's rooms. Dr requested three lots of blood tests from me a while ago. Still up to today, I never recieved a telephone call from Dr's office, explaining why all the blood tests. In fact I received a letter from Dr's rooms explaining that there is some kidney damage. This was after the second lot of bloods they took. I made appointment with local Dr's rooms, a while ago, as I started menopause and lots of family stress.

So there is a huge difference between the Uk and South Africa. Uk has the NHS. Most big companies in South Africa have what one would call a partner "medical aid". It's compulsory for mostly big companies to join a "medical aid company" on behalf of their employees. Some companies pay half of the cost for "medical aid" Like my son-in law's company. Other big companies, an employee pays the the full amount which is deducted from your salary on a monthly basis. My husband paid the full amount for both of us at the IT company we both worked at before we both got made redundant. An employee can also choose which level of medical aid they want within the same "medical aid" company that the company you work for choose. My husband chose the second highest level. Cos then it covers hospital as well, besides him being diabetic. One can choose if they just cover medicine and no hospital, vice versa or both. Most "medical aids" also have an option for "chronic meds" which one does not pay for, the "medical aid" pays for it. Me been HIV, I was put on "chronic meds". Some of the medication that my husband is on for diabetic, that was also considered "chronic medication".

So having a "medical aid" is what one would call a savings account. All depends which "medical aid" one goes on, and what level, the more one uses the less the amount on the "medical aid" becomes available. This is yearly. So for instance one goes on "medical aid" say at the end of February. It will expire the following year at the end of February. If one uses all the funds in the "medical aid" before the end of the year is up. You have to pay for all the Dr's and medical bills yourself. Some bills, one can claim from tax in South Africa. There is also a time frame in order to submit all your Dr's and medical bills to SARS(South African Revenue Service). Tax man.

There is government hospitals and clinics in South Africa, that one can attend if one is ill or needs an operation or for emergencies if one is not on "medical aid". But I am sorry to say I personally wouldn't like to attend to them. They are in dire straits. But if a person hasn't got an option. Then it's the way to go.

The NHS

by Barry Wilkinson

As a Patient.

The NHS is my saviour, my surrogate mother, my succour. It's the organisation that saved my life. It looks after me, it never lets me down. When I was young it was strict. Up early, washed, preened. All ironed sheets and hospital corners. Task, task task. Strict demarcation between doctor and nurse. Now it is all about efficiency. The drive to maximise use. Less qualified staff. Nurses performing roles that once only a doctor did. Unqualified nurses performing roles that once only the qualified did. People move faster. I see strain.

As a Nurse.

The NHS is my employer. It is the greatest ideal of my life. Created because people do not become Ill out of spite. Because a poor person is entitled to the same health as a rich person. I used to be less busy, had more time, but was encouraged to scrub, clean and fill time. Don't sit on the bed, don't stop to talk. Now I am much more busier. I have to do more with less. I have more skills but more responsibility and less time to use them. I am encouraged to talk to patients but don't have time to do so. I supervise unqualified nurses performing roles I once did. I see less of patients and more of computer screens and data.

Why we need the NHS

by Mark Barham

I have been dealing with the NHS all my life, for when I started out on this life I weighed 1lb 13 oz as I was 8 week premature. I was in hospital for the first 8 months of my life, I can only imagine the care I received from the amazing medical team. I can't remember back then as I was too young and fragile. I had pneumonia it's probably why I have stayed small at 5 foot 7.

I can remember cracking my head open while out hunting for conkers, yes im that old. My friends were chucking sticks into the tree and I was collecting the conkers, however one hit my head and there was panic, I was rushed to hospital, I can still feel the bump or scar on my head.

It wasn't until 1997 that I found out I really need the NHS was when I got diagnosed HIV positive.

I have experienced many NHS Trusts around the country, I had a chest infection while I was living in London, I was placed in a room on my own linked up to all these machines, I think it was not long after I was diagnosed. I've always been treated with dignity and compassion. Yes I may have waited to go into appointments but I have always said , the doctors and nurses are very busy, they will get to me eventually.

I can remember a friend who lived above me in my flat in Southampton. John was on the board of trustees at the Ribbons Centre, the local HIV support centre. We lived in a block of 4 flats which were given to people suffering from HIV. He went into hospital with a brain haemorrhage and he was at that time going out with my Ex. It was a horrendous but hilarious at the same time for me and Stuart. The matron would keep us waiting to go see john, so we watched staff members put the door code in the thing on the wall. The words 'How did you get that code' is still remembered to this day.

After losing my sister Linda, John was one of many friends to die from HIV. I lost my dad 10 years ago, after he went in for a hernia operation.

More recently I have needed the services when I have received the covid jabs and their boosters.

That meant I had to go to Durham, Newcastle and gay pride of all places to get my last booster, the boosters were all in NHS medical vehicles all with the same amazing staff. I have been lucky, I have not had any side effects from any of the jabs.

Overall my experiences with the NHS has always been positive, I'm still alive after 51 years so that has to be a good thing right.

National Health Service and Me

by Nick Hargreaves

My experience with the NHS goes back a long way, right back to when I was a kid so let's start at the bottom shall we and work up to the present day.

My earliest memory of the NHS was having an ultrasound scan when I was about seven. I remember waiting to have the scan and one of the doctors approaching me and my mam in the waiting area and saying to my mam, "he looks a bit worried." He then went on to say that all the procedure involved was rubbing some gel into the abdomen and using the scanning device to carry out the task in hand and that made me feel a lot more reassured.

At around about the same age, I had to go to the general hospital in town I think it was, to have five baby teeth taken out that had gone bad. This was done under general anesthetic and was no problem as I didn't feel a thing. I just remember the head member of staff saying Breathe through your nose then I woke up spitting blood and the rest is history. I actually got off lightly because I was meant to have seven teeth taken out but for some reason they narrowed it down to just five. That's the price you pay for having a sweet tooth and not brushing your teeth properly as a kid I guess. Still, at least they were only milk teeth.

As an early teenager, I discovered a lump on my left testicle. This was before all the talk about testicular cancer became prominent so I thought nothing of it. It turned out just to be a varicus vein in the scrotum so happy days.

From the age of thirteen I started to suffer from depression. I remember my first trip to my GP about it and I was with my mam at the time and he told me that if you think that there is a pill that will make that go away you're very much mistaken. However on my second visit to see him about it, he put me on an antidepressant called Citalopram. I think he thought that it was going to be a recurring thing with me so he put me on tablets.

Aged fifteen I had the equivalent of three nervous breakdowns where I was hospitalised for two to three weeks for each one. Firstly in the children's ward of Rake Lane Hospital then in the General Hospital up in town and lastly in the Sir Martin Roth Young Person's Unit (YPU) which was located just next to the General Hospital. At the time we didn't know what caused the illness and neither did the doctors, which was a bit frightening looking back. We clutched at a few straws. A growth spurt, artifical sweeteners, one or two others. Looking back now I strongly think that the two years of depressive episodes beforehand did something to my brain to cause them. In the end I was just glad to pull through and after the third episode was over the doctor at the YPU, Dr Ward I think his name was, put me on a mood stabiliser called Sodium Valproate and I haven't had a relapse since then.

However depression and mental health never really escaped me as now I am diagnosed with bipolar. What caused my diagnosis was an ongoing feud between my grandma and my dad which was left unresolved. I got my diagnosis in the summer of 2008 and it's been a learning curve believe me. I've made a few mistakes and upset a few people but I've put it all down to experience. Since then I've had prostatitis which I'm on tablets for and the pain has gone so that's about it. That's all the important stuff anyway. I've left out a couple of things like my nose job and my cystoscopy as they didn't really make for interesting reading but that was the main things that I wanted to talk about.

Let's see what the future holds, eh? Stay well.

Happy Calm Cosy

by Fatal Whimsy

Something that I've always *hated* about mental health care places is, the pretentious, "happy, calm, cosy" atmosphere that they try to create.

"Happy", smiley-face art and bright colours all over the place, "calm" pictures on the walls and "cosy" sofas. Who the *hell* are they trying to kid!? All of this is a *complete* and utter *contradiction*.

As you sit in this "happy, calm, cosy" waiting room, you see someone with their carer trying to comfort them, in that overly understanding, high pitched, 'talking to a child' voice. Others look miserable, anxious or trapped. Someone is sobbing in the corner.

Time passes *slowly*. Drs *stride* in with their "happy, calm, cosy" voice. *Always* late, which is *NOT* "happy, calm," or "cosy."

This environment *DOES NOT* make me "happy." If I was happy I wouldn't need to be here.

It *DOES NOT* make me "calm." If I was calm, I wouldn't be on mood stabilizers. I wouldn't be getting monitored closely by your pretentious, "happy, calm, cosy" voice, as if the risk of a *fatal* skin condition is *not* a big deal. Your "calm" voice does *not* make this risk, a "calm" risk.

Your "calm" pictures of a boat on a stream and your "cosy" sofa, scream with comedic "*IRONY!*"

The only "*real*" thing here is the box of handkerchiefs on the table. The rest of this *safe-space* movie set makes me "anxious, untrusting" and "*un*comfortable!"

The only place where this atmosphere is genuine, is The Recovery College Collective. Here, the staff and volunteers have *lived* experience, so there's less need to pretend to understand. They just listen to me and if they don't understand, they ask me.

They *don't* speak to me in that pretentious, "happy, calm cosy" voice. They don't treat me from a medical journal, or as an invalid. They treat me as a *capable* person. They treat me from the *heart*. They *accept* my sadness and allow me to feel ok with not being ok. They help me to take one tiny step, or more, out of my low headspace, at my own pace.

They *welcome* me, to a whole new world of peer support activities, with other people just like me. They *empower* me, to build my own personal journey to recovery. They support me, to overcome the difficulties that this task holds. They teach me, how to self-soothe, self-care and gain self-insight. They show me, how to use distress tolerance and relaxation techniques, to manage life's challenges.

Even when I'm *not* "happy, calm," or "cosy", I still associate this place, this ReCoCo, with comforting feelings. It is my *safe* space, where I can be, whatever I feel, without judgement, even when I'm *not* "happy, calm, cosy". So in a way, Recoco *is* "happy, calm, cosy", because they *don't* force me to *be* "happy, calm," or "cosy".

Diagnosis

by Mary Pickin

And lo she was summonsed to the Breast Assessment Clinic.
Behold the serious looks, the suppressed tears
The anger, the fear of the demon, carcinoma
Was Yahweh with her?
Yahweh, the loving father,
The jealous God
The bosomless one

And lo she was anointed with oil and ultra sounded by Prophetess
The sacrificial needle pierced her breast
And she babbled incoherently in her fear of flight
And she was sent out into the Desert
For forty minutes and forty minutes more
And she wait for Moses to come down from the mountain

And lo Moses came down from the mountain
And sat with her sombre husband and the smiling
Breast Care Nurse and saith
"There's no easy way to tell you this"

And into the vale tears went she,
Into the Tunnel of Wilde Excision Biopsy,
Haematoma, Tamoxifen, Radiotherapy.
Into the valley of death and lo she thought
Why don't I think,
'I've got my life to lead, things to do, poems to write
Projects to complete, places to go?'

Why do I just want to hide under a duvet?

Amen

A Place

Pick a place that means something to you.

"A place where we built chances together."

Head space
by Mary Pickin

A wall in Heaton where, drunk
I bashed my head again and again
To stop the brain chaos
To prove a point
'I'm hurting, you lied
This is how bad I feel'

A bench in Cullercoats gazing
Out to sea. It's vastness
A comfort; it's unrelenting continuity
Inspiring. I'm still in the moment
My brain bathed by the breeze
This is how good I feel

Cresswell Beach
by Sarah Gunn

The place I feel safe is Cresswell Beach.
When I was ill I liked to walk along the beach, listening to the sea.
I like the coast and looking at the sea. I used to go every week with my partner.
It makes me feel safe being by the coast.
And calm and peaceful.
I don't go out so much now as I don't have a car.
Sometime I will bus there again.

I enjoy walking along the coast.
It helps my mental health and wellbeing being by the coast.
As I was brought up by the sea in Whitley Bay.
I enjoyed living by the sea as a child.

On the coast

by Victoria Gray

I'd disappeared for a few weeks. I'd just started university and my mental health torpedoed.

A student from Newcastle University had signed up to the peer mentor programme. I was assigned to her. She reached out after I had missed a meeting, maybe more.

We agreed to meet at Nando's. Sitting opposite her I felt like my brain had just exploded and I'd been left to carry on without it.

After opening up about what had been going on with me she told me about a place called Cullercoats and told me it's where she goes to think when things get too much. She told me you can get there on the metro from South Gosforth, the place where my student accommodation was.

I didn't understand the metro yet, it had lots of stops, different coloured lines, and some of the names sounded funny. I felt like I had moved to London.

I did manage to get myself there though.

The journey's weird when you are so unwell, nobody else knows what you're going through. I was sat with an exploded brain amongst seemingly normal people.

In hindsight I'm aware now that there were probably others going through the pain I was feeling too.

After getting there I sat down on a bench and realised why Allie came here. It was stunning, and quiet.

That's the important bit. Quiet.

My mind felt soothed, I was still troubled but looking out at where the sea meets the horizon I was reminded of the town I grew up in close to the coast, I noticed the house to the left - thinking how brilliant it would look on a postcard. The wind bit a bit but I liked it, it forced the fresh air on me and god knows I needed it. Sometimes when things get too much it's hard to remind yourself when you need a break, Cullercoats did that for me.

Cullercoats is now a place I frequent often, I cite it myself as one of the best bits of Newcastle's coast. I take joy in being there, on my own, with friends, with family.

Dr Larry Gurney, Arnold and Ernest in their van 'Emily'

Jackdaws, Pink Rooms and Sunflowers

by Dr Larry Gurney

After discharge from hospital I was home without a diagnosis and at 3pm in June the health advisor came to my house and I was still ill in bed. The ugly room was pink. I remember the bed low to the ground and the sound of the jackdaws crawing and she gave me my diagnosis.

I hated that room. I hated the jackdaws. I have always hated *pink*.
My health advisor and I attempted to drink whiskey. Disgusting stuff.

Safe space two. One in the UK is my van. I have travelled all over in it since 2014. Since 2018 it has become my studio on wheels. I sat in it and cried after Bob died last year and it is a comfort because it gave me a safe toilet on wheels if I need it. A soft bed when I need to sleep and a place to cry and be creative.

The other is the first centre we built in South Africa in Kaysna. Where for the first time in 10 years at least I felt part of some community, not my own because I don't think one exists in the UK but a place where we built chances together, painted art together and formed the only family I've had.

Diagnosed. There is no place to go when diagnosed, everywhere is empty without life and future. Diagnoses took away my chance to be a father. Normality melted. I have never recovered from that personal loss, no place could have held me at that stage.

My pink room I now love. It's full of my sunflower paintings and is yellow and bright.
I now have a hole in the wall so I never feel locked in, in which I have now a stained glass I made. My van has changed a little after Bob died, I had no confidence in her.
MAD centre I have been away too long from and I don't know the new families or kids.

There are few rooms in my house with solid walls, each has a window. Some have windows on the inner walls and outer walls. I must have the sun in as much of my little house as I can.
I can live in a van, I have no attachment to places. I would rather be in Dorset or London to feel really safe.

Safe is hard. HIV traps you in health settings so you can no longer live anywhere in the world.

So safe yes but trapped also.

A place

by David Oliver

Here I am again. Head too heavy to lift, bones to sore to move. How long has it been? Days, Weeks? I can't continue to function at this level. Dark days lie ahead. I need to rest. I need to move. I need to be around people. Am I safe on my own? Look at this place. It's a mess. My life is struggling to move forward. We've reached a stalemate. I don't deserve food. I don't deserve love. I don't deserve to be happy.

I need to Move. Just a little. Just outside. If I can roll out of bed, I can get a shower. I can go outside. I can try and just for once. My batteries are flat. I need to do something. Trapped and wrapped in my fortress of solitude. Surely it won't take long. Just a little bit further. I think I can make it. Just a few more tears to shed. A few more hours of dread. Heart racing. Head Foggy. Limbs flat. Chemically Imbalanced. Surely if. But when. What if. But how.

Recharge. Release. Rage. Frustration. Destiny. Desire. Hope. Loss. Fear. Swirling. Cascading. Control. Spiralling. Losing. Hoping. Wishing. Yearning. Falling. Clashing. Non-Functioning. Useless. Flooding. Medication. Timing. Acid. Burning. Binge. Guilty. Wrestling. Desire. Destiny. Rage.

Slowly.
Caring.
Enough.
Worthy.
Again.
Repeat.

East End, West End

by Barry Wilkinson

West End, School.

I am
Stinky kid
Smelly boy
Pissy pants

But
I am
Righter of wrongs
Justice for the chair bound
I am
Strongman
Speedy boy
I am
Footballer
Brainbox
One eyed in the land of the blind

East End, Home.

I am
Hidden life
Quiet
Shy boy
I am
The guy with a secret

But
I am
Cared for
Worried over

Hospice

by Mary O'Sullivan-Fawcett

As we cautiously entered the building
We were terrified
That word, hospice, frightened you so much
But we said we'd look
And you had already said you'd never go again

The welcome we received was filled with love
Open hearts and open arms
There was no flinching from the truth
And that's what we needed
We really hadn't realised that

It was safe, our haven
We could trust everyone
You made lovely friends who you didn't have to explain anything to
They understood, they had their own concerns
And the laughter was joyous, it made my heart sing

You went to day hospice
Closely followed by me, I found your care hard to let go
If I wasn't with you I struggled
I found out you only settled there if I was nearby
And so they got a two for one deal

Eventually you needed to stay in for a while
They gave us a room
They looked after us both
I hadn't known I needed looking after too
Our days there were filled with love and tears, and laughter

Places associate with illness

by C.L

There are quite a few places I associate with my illness. The first would be the monument in Newcastle where I was taken into custody by the police as my mother reported me as a missing person.

I was taken back to my mothers and she would not let me live at home. So eventually the police sectioned me under the mental health act.

This place, Monument, I no longer think of as bad. It is just used as a meeting place for all kinds of people. I consider Newcastle a safe place as do I the various hospitals I have been in.

Yes my view has definitely changed over time as I no longer think about these events because they were in the past and you can't change the past. but you can move on and see things as they are.

Other places I associate with my past are Gateshead hospital, Newcastle hospital and the north London clinic. I actually enjoyed London a fair bit even though I did not realise it at the time. Meet some nice people down there. Patients and staff who I all got on well with.

The nicotine is what got me through this experience, also talking and meeting new people from a different part of the UK.

Music helped a lot too. There was always a new track to download on to an mp3 player.

We had internet access and occupational therapy, I brushed up on my math skills with one of the staff members who was a dedicated maths tutor.

I asked the doctor 'what do I need to get home'. He said 'do occupational therapy' and so I did and enjoyed it, and eventually I was released from a different hospital closer to home. That being St Nicks in Newcastle where I also did occupational therapy and managed to get unescorted leave and eventually released back into society.

I have been free for about 3 or more years. I plan to stay free and become a decent member of society.

The bad place

by Steve Wood

So many stops along the way
The infrequent, the occasional, the everyday
At home I feel my patience fray
Frustration boiling over, unable to keep my fury at bay

At work, when it seemed I might be overcome
When the enormity of what I faced had struck me dumb
When I've been unable to control my traitorous thumb
Let alone my arm, and leg, and foot, all numb

With friends, yet still alone
The restless spirit of the man I was
Whispering into the howling wind of grievous loss
Self pity gnawing at me, e'en unto bone

Yet none of these has yet compared
To the wretchedness and dark despair
Of a single hour in a one horse town.
By rights I shouldn't give a fuck
About the place that we call Crook.

Shortly after I'd been told
My painful story yet to unfold
I stood with friends in bitter cold
To preach the socialist message
I figured for at least a while
I'd lose the frown, dust off the smile
I'd try to go the extra mile
To rid us of the true blue menace

A man approached , around my age
I smiled and asked him how he'd vote
His face betrayed the sudden change
The spiral into spit-flecked rage
Demanded that I tell him
Where socialism had ever worked
So, with confidence I did not feel
And my best "winning grin"
I told him tales of Sweden, Denmark and those crazy, commie Finns
He might have attacked my political beliefs
He might have chosen violence
Instead he struck at the heart of my grief
Dropped a bomb into my self-indulgent silence
Rather than debate
Rather than be good
He commented upon my tremor
And he opened up a flood
Of righteous fury
This one man, right wing judge and jury
Simply couldn't play it fair
And I'm reminded of my weakness
And what bastards men can be
Whenever I am there.

Centre of Excellence

by Maxine Patterson

The place for me that has such a special meaning is The Freeman Hospital in Newcastle upon Tyne. It's the Centre of Excellence for Neuroendocrine Cancer, the only one in the North of England. Leeds is the next nearest.

The Freeman is where I was rushed to in 2015 when my condition deteriorated and I had to undergo a massive operation as an emergency. I felt safe and confident in the surgical and medical teams. They are so professional and I was well treated but I always associate that hospital with the life changing aspects of that operation and the long painful recuperation afterwards.

I attend the NET clinic at the Freeman, and I see the consultant and the Specialist Nurse. They are efficient and caring, but so very, very busy. I feel like an object on a conveyor belt, even though all the staff there try very hard to be caring and helpful.

I'm learning to be more proactive, making detailed notes on the issues I want clarification on and that way getting a more positive outcome from my in my clinic appointments. That way the Freeman Hospital becomes a place where I matter, not a place where I am a passive object being dealt with.

How does it feel to talk?

To talk, to think, to share, to write.

"A sea of mismatched words that somehow form words and sentences."

Bob Hoskins

by Nick Hargreaves

I think that it feels very good to talk, to share your feelings and thoughts with anyone who is a good listener. Company can be a very good thing but on the other hand I am a person who does long for a bit of solitude. I love spending time in my room listening to my music, the only problem with that is that the intrusive thoughts just keep on coming. You/I don't get them if you are talking to someone as talking is a great distraction.

I've always found talking very easy, I can be very chatty when I want to be. I've always spoken to someone when I've felt vulnerable.

I've had a lot of support concerning my mental health over the years, from the likes of family, friends and teachers. The only change in my ability to talk about something now is more along the physical side of things as it concerns the actual speed of my speech. With now having bi-polar, the mania side of my condition has taken over and overall I would say that I speak quicker now than I have ever done in the past. Other than that I don't think there's been any changes in my ability to talk to someone if I need help support or guidance. I've always been able to talk. I think I get it from my mam as she is very chatty and sociable, always has been.

I remember when Jack died, she talked to just about anyone about it. Her friends, Jane's friends, even neutral people like people who worked in shops in town and places like that. Just before I got diagnosed with bi-polar, I talked to a lot of people as well. I spent a lot of time at my local pub where my friends there were very supportive and I saw a lot of parallels in people, mainly in Sam and Paula, my two friends at the time who compared to my parents were a lot more down to earth and foot loose and fancy free. I have a very vivid memory about asking them if they worried in general about their son Mike and the reason I asked them this was because my parents especially at the time worried a lot more about me and Sam pretty much said in a nutshell that they did as well concerning Mike and that they were very grateful to receive either a text or a phone call just to reassure them that he was safe.

Take my advice, when you're feeling a bit low or a bit vulnerable or lonely, talk to someone, you'd be surprised how good it feels. Like Bob Hoskins said in the 1990s BT adverts, "it's good to talk."

The Journey

by Ian Watson

Sitting with these unknown emotions,
a sense of release overcomes me as they spill out into a sea
of mismatched words that somehow form words and sentences

The understanding in another's actions and face,
there is no better love
I don't know exactly, But I do know what you feel,
I know; such a powerful embrace

Through wisdom comes courage, the sage reflected
Forever winding and bending, this journey I share
It is still mine and mine alone

Self-edited but still holding true,
Confident and empowered
The knowing of warmth

I am now the other, awaiting the sea of unknown emotions
With arms of understanding simply saying
I'm here

Chatterbox

by Mark Barham

It's good to talk, well I find I get a great deal from it. It makes me happy to converse with my friends, you can express so many feelings, sadness, happiness, laughter and comforting. I get a great deal from talking.

I have never been a shy person, so I think that helps. I love to talk to people that struggle, or I have not met before. When I have been at various support centres, I have been asked to talk to new people coming for the I first time. Just to make them feel comfortable.

I used to do school talks, talking about HIV and me of which I'm good at, I think it is good to spread the happier side of dealing with HIV. It's also great for people to hear from someone dealing with it, not just hearing statistics.

When dealing with friends and family, it is a lot harder to talk about HIV, you are not sure on their reaction and your hoping to get all the information correct, you don't want to create panic with them. When I got diagnosed in 1997 a lot of people were still dying, not nowadays thank god, this has been helped with the range of tablets available.

Because I can remember most of my memories, I find it very easy. It also helps that I feel comfortable talking about dealing with it. I suppose it could be said it's how I cope with dealing with it, I'm not sure.

All my friends tell me I'm very chatty and can talk forever. My sense of humour helps, I think. I always try and make people smile and open up to me. I talk about silly things at first, just to make them comfortable and when I think they are ready, I delve a bit deeper and that gets the conversation going.

I have enjoyed the writing group so much, as it allowed us to talk and remember stuff. It's easy I suppose because we have grown as a group and got used to everyone. We have a nice core group.

The only time I find it difficult is when I must be confrontational. I'm not an angry person so I find that is quite hard. Trying to find that emotion is difficult for me because I'm not used to it. I try and deal with it constructively

I talk to my elderly neighbours, not about HIV but just to check on them. It gives them a bit of company, someone to talk to. As many of them will not see anybody except their carers.

Talking about HIV

by Pauline Hass

For me, talking to my family about HIV, is very difficult, as I kept my HIV status secret from them. Not sure why. But I can openly discuss my status with my husband and my best friend, Cheryl and now my next door neighbour, Lorraine, who has become a very dear friend to me and haven't known her for long, as we only moved to North Shields 7 months ago. I can't remember actually when I first became friends with Lorraine. To me, telling a complete stranger is easier than telling my family.

I have known Karen for maybe just over a year, and I still haven't told her either, and my 2 other friends that I met. Karen is staying over this coming weekend. So I might tell her, if the timing is right. Will see how it goes.

Suppose sometime I will tell my family. If I do tell them. I want to tell them together, at the moment I can't as both my sister and daughter is still in South Africa. My son is in the UK.

I think the reason as to why I didn't tell my family, is because it will spread like wild fire. Tanya will tell her friends, some of them I know, same with my son-in-law. My son's partner, Ana, is portuguese and is very close to her family, and she will also tell them all, cousins included. I think, Judith, my sister will be shocked. I know Judith, every time I get sick, she will most probably ask me is it to do with HIV as she is a worrier.

Judith is not well herself and not in a very good space at the moment. She lost her husband 3 years ago on the 18th September after been married for 49 years. Last year on the 2nd November 2022 she lost her oldest son, Christopher, as 52, had a stroke. In between loosing her husband and son, she also lost a bird(cockatel) that she had for over for 10 years and her little maltese dog also passed away. So in 3 years, she lost 2 humans and 2 animals. At this point, I don't want to add extra burdens on her. I don't want her to worry about me. And if I did tell her, she will also tell the rest of her family and friends.

I have a lot to think about.

On the same page

by Victoria Gray

It helps with the loneliness mental illness brings to talk with likeminded people.

They understand where I'm coming from and that things aren't always simple. The simple things are often actually what's most complicated

I've done a lot of talking the past few years so sometimes I feel like a broken record, actually.
A lot of the time.

As time goes on there are parts I don't like discussing as they're no longer relevant to my identity. I'd like to leave them behind.

Unfortunately the nature of talking means they can come up.

Sometimes after talking I can feel a dull ache eating me up inside that there's things deep down which don't come out.
Things no one knows. And that can feel soul destroying. At times.

Advice

What advice do you give to someone who's just been diagnosed
with the same condition as yourself?

*"You will feel better; you may not think it now
but I guarantee you will."*

Never give in

by Liz Parkinson

There she is, lost in a dark place

consumed by fear and terror.

It's physical as well, she is in pain and her eyes are unusually bright.

She sits there; arms wrapped around herself

and what do I say? How can I offer hope?

I know what it's like, I tell her, you must remember bad things do pass.

Hang on and never give in

Talk to me or be silent.

It's okay to be ill, to feel the dark dread.

I will stay with you I will keep you safe and

we will be together when the light comes.

Sit on a Bench

by Mary Pickin

First of all, you *will* feel better; you may not think it now but I guarantee you will.

Medication really helps me; it may very well help you. Be prepared to try different kinds; every one of us has a unique

brain which may benefit from a wide range of drugs.

You can avoid medication if you want to. Replace it with physical exercise, meditation, good nutrition and, if you're brave, wild water swimming. I'd rather be depressed myself.

There are lots of organisations who can help, both online and off. Talking therapies has helped me a lot.

Beware of so-called friends who avoid you when you're not well- they are stupid and not worth bothering with for the present. People will listen to you; you will definitely find out who your real friends are. That's a good thing. Someone on the periphery of your life is likely to help you best. That's a lovely surprise.

You may think your family and/or friends will be better off without you when things are really bad. This is a delusion. Instead sit up in bed, eat chocolates and a sweet sherry or some sort of liqueur and imagine your funeral and think how sorry everyone will be who hurt your feelings. This wallowing and is a healthy one off activity.

Write things down if you can. Vent on paper or record yourself venting. Shout in the shower, dance in the mud (not in front of people); swear if needs be.

If you can, sit on a bench and watch the sea or little birds and flowers. See how you're both huge alongside the little birds and flowers and miniscule in relation to the sea.

Check out the clouds and breathe.

Zoe Robinson and her notebook

Sweets and shoes

by Zoe Robinson

Crafting your recovery is like filling a bag from the pick 'n' mix sweets counter.

I could give you advice by listing all the things that have helped me: the psychotherapies, the alternative therapies, the physiotherapies, the nutrition, the meditation, the brain hacks and habits, the spiritual practice, and the medications. But you must explore what works for your unique combination of family history, personality traits, values, life experiences, brain wiring and physiology.

Every time I discover a new tool to shape my illness into a more palatable form, I become excited. My current obsession is 'Internal Family Systems' therapy. It is helping me identify the parts of my personality that are fighting against each other, creating self-sabotage and paralysis.

Recently, I had a long discussion with my internal critic, the part which has been torturing me multiple times a day, for decades. I am having some success:

Yesterday I was walking in my new trainers which are a little too big. Instead of beating myself up about how stupid I was for buying those shoes, and how I was wasting money and how I could injure myself and how I should be ashamed of myself for being imperfect and how I should kill myself, a thought popped into my head - a non-judgemental suggestion that I could simply buy some insoles.

It seems that I have convinced my hypercritical part to change its tone from shaming vitriol into calm advice!

Letter to Alan

by Mark Barham

Dear Alan,

After you informed me of your HIV diagnosis, I felt I should write you this letter for some tips on how to deal with the news. I just wanted to start to say thank you for disclosing it to me and having the courage to do that. What you will learn is once you've told someone, it is forever out there, i.e., on social media, friends or family. Just take your time so you can get used to your diagnosis. Its up to you when or if you disclose.

The first thing I would say is Don't worry, HIV is not regarded as life threatening anymore, like it was in the 80's. When you start the medication, if you don't miss doses, you could live a long happy life. I say happy because you need to try and stay positive. I know its hard to when you have just heard this news, but please try. Its ok to feel anxious and be frightened, you would not be a fabulous human being that you are without those feelings. Always try and speak to someone about them. Your GP, friends like myself. You will always have a shoulder to cry on with me fella.

Regarding medication, there will be side affects however these will decrease over time, I don't want you to worry with a list of them, your doctor will explain if you ask. Don't look up things on the internet i.e. side effects, everyone is different, I have not had any for years now. Try and get yourself one of those pillboxes, it will help to sort your pills out, you can get them from your Doctor or any cheap shop.

Hopefully you will be able to reach out to family and friends like I did. You have made a fantastic start by telling me. Don't hesitate to contact me if you have any concerns. I have had HIV for 25 years now and have loads of stories to tell you, hopefully these and other suggestions I have mentioned will help you over the coming months. One thing that has definitely helped me is local support groups. They are a bunch of people who also have HIV and fantastic staff and volunteers. You will find you can talk to others about HIV and hopefully elevate any worries. It will improve your social life too.

Always remember you are in charge of your own mind and body. Here are those suggestions.

- Try and get a pill box
- Locate a local HIV support Group
- Never diagnose yourself from the internet
- Side effects will not last forever
- Stay positive

Big hugs.

Love always,

Mark

Dear J

by Dr Larry Gurney

Dear J,

I heard you were just given the news you are 'positive'. How are you feeling? I wish I could be there to spend a bit of time with you to see if I could add anything to what you may have heard or had been thinking the last 24 hours. I'm sorry I wasn't in when you phoned, however, I'm glad you felt strong enough to leave the message on the answer phone. I have, by the way, erased the message. Not that anyone would listen to it other than me! Telling someone is a brave choice, but I assume you told me simply because you know I have been +ve the last 30 years.

I'd say firstly just be careful at first who you tell. There is a need I think to choose carefully, those who you trust with the information. We should be a long way forward on the issue than we are, but sadly we still have to preserve our information. Not a lot has changed in this regard. Sometimes it is easier to speak with professional help to get some support on some of the issues you mentioned on the phone, although I'm happy to help but each journey is unique and whilst I have some experience, it is my own. That is always the case with everyone and your experience is yours.

I realise you have anxieties about what to do next. Stop, breathe a bit and take some time. You have plenty, as much as you ever had the day before you knew. The diagnosis you have is, as you know with my experience, not likely to change you too much as a person in terms of you living life.

Sure, you might want to make some changes to you but any life challenge makes that a possibility. As many now realise, the meds are less likely to cause you any illness. Your generation has been on PREP for a while. But I don't know these days if the idea is to start early. I have often felt it best simply because even with meds the virus does take out sections of your immune menu so jumping on it fast may preserve what you have. It's harder to re-teach the immune system than it is to preserve if the virus targets them.

Don't let this bother you too much - your consultant will do a lot more tests to help you out.

Then you mentioned work. I know you are concerned about who needs to know. But you are not doing any invasive interventions so the precautions you took last week are the same as the ones next week.

It is fear that becomes the trait that does more harm than the reality. So talk about it with anyone you have so far had a good response from. Again if you tell someone make sure you are quite clear with the expectation that telling them you expect confidentiality. Sometimes people need this reinforced so be clear.

It's plus 30 years now for me. I've had my ups and downs but the biggest challenge for me has been unknown changing information. You're now in a group of people who pretty much can rely on the generations that have gone before. We pretty much rely on the fact that with medication a newly diagnosed person can live a great life as great at least as it was before yesterday's news.

So know I am always around to chat with, and if you need a shoulder to cry on, a person to laugh with and an "expert" to discuss with practical issues I am HERE.

So don't hesitate. Be well and accept any change that is dramatic takes a time to transition. Take care, Best Wishes.

Advice

by Gift

Hello, my name is Gift
It's not the end of your life

She should welcome it
She going to be alright
You must be strong
Tell a trusted friend
Virus is loading again
It's going to be serious
This problem is not mine only
You are on the safe side
Do not think too much about it

Without Blue Sky Trust, I'd be a dead person
Blue Sky Trust was my big bone to lean on
When I'm crying they comfort me
When I go home I'm happy again
It's not the end of your life
As long as you take your mediation
Everything will be okay

Hopes for the future

A hopeful sign-off from our writers.

"I want glory, smiles. I want to be noticed."

Hello Gorgeous

by Mary Pickin

I hope that I will shed my grudges like a snake sloughs its skin

I hope I stop fixating on my poor old mum who,

God knows, had her own troubles

I hope to research my heritage to see I'm not alone on my madness

I hope my hunger will move from the taste and comfort of food and move to something else - this is a faint hope

I hope to take more pride in my home and appearance and take control my budget and my single life.

I hope that the rush of joy I experience when looking at petals on flowers, birds' plumage and the blackbird's song and the moon on the sea at midnight on New Year's Eve never stops so that every day I can look in the mirror first thing and say "Hello gorgeous, what adventures shall we go on today?

Hope

by Isabel Marafao

Hope. I'm hopeful of the NHS. Health is well, manageable by doctors. Give me safety all the time. Making me exam all my diseases but I need to let you know that HIV is the one more stable than the rest.

Family. Love, care, truth, fun, good time. They give me strength to keep going.

I have friendship. I'm ok with friends. I've a lot of good friends. I need their love to make me a happier person.

I'm positive, I'm blessed and I'm lucky. I'm codependent of love. A

Confidence, I don't have any

by Dr Larry Gurney

I would love the confidence to believe in myself in order to one day find a job which would fill me with pride, allow me to discover again who I am. I'd like to see an end to discrimination, I'd like to learn to smile again to return to optimism to be positive again. What has changed? Maybe that needs to be discovered first so performing the first step is to answer why. I'd hope to be able to one day contribute to people's lives. How can a man who spent his whole life fighting oppression from the age of 16 have become so inactive.

From *activism* to *inactivism*. What happened?

Pain happened, I think. As I left africa the chemo for my life took me to the darkest most painful space, 5 years in the darkness post treatment, suicidal and black extreme and empty. My love of life drained and sank away and I just can't find it anymore. The sepsis in 2020 showed me how close one can get to death and it scares me how impossibly difficult it is to live with a feeling that you are dispensable. The NHS showed me that the people you should be able to trust are not trusted. I realise I live in fear of the NHS, not illness.

I wish I could get private health care to feel safe again. The world is dangerous and when a person and when a person has to fight to survive the desire to be active to help the world has to be turned inwards, to save oneself. So it makes me feel selfish, a feeling I don't like to feel.

My hope would be to move South, when I am in the South I feel safe. Probably not but it's a fantasy hope. I hope to learn freedom and style in my art. That joy, I hope would bring some joy to people.

Hope. An idea that relies on luck too much.

Tomorrow

by Maxine Patterson

My hopes for the future are necessarily linked to my life now. I don't want to climb the highest mountain; I'm sure I could get up, not so sure about getting down again. I certainly don't want to lie on a sun kissed beach somewhere, because I can't stand the heat anymore. I would love to do a trip to the Artic again and see the Northern Lights, but that would be an incidental treat, not really a hope for the future.

My hopes for the future are mundane, safe, boring ones. My hopes involve continuing to live with my Cancer and having a reasonable quality of life. Quality not quantity!

My hopes involve spending time with my son, showing him how much I care for him without making him feel uncomfortable and beholden to me.

My hopes involve living with my husband and showing him how much I care for him and love him, even when he really, really annoys me.

My hopes involve being fit enough to continue working in our garden, looking after the insects and creatures that have become a part of our lives.

My biggest hope for the future is to not become selfish and self centred. Sometimes, when we get old and in pain, we forget to thank and acknowledge those around us to help us.

I want

by Mary O'Sullivan-Fawcett

I want to live the best life I can
To keep the demons that crowd my mind at bay To fight with the other
illnesses that plague me And win at least one battle a day

I want to be able to stand upright & breathe To have music fill my soul
To spend time with family & friends
To laugh loud & long

And to one day meet my love again
I know he's waiting for me at the rollercoaster

It's not much but it will do me!

Tomorrow

by David Slater

Tomorrow will soon arrive,
Be announced, and stride in,
Swathed in its usual folds,
Masked; as ever a mystery.

Tomorrow will unveil itself,
Showing smiles and frowns,
Bearing the gifts it has made,
And offer these, open-handed.

I shall be rewarded by that present,
And shall return my own gifts,
Of today remembered, and
Yesterday restored, renewed.
ll kind of love. To be alive.

C.L's favourite rings

Future Hopes

by C.L

My hopes for the future are simple.

To reduce my medication first then plan out what to do from there.

I would like to be on 5mg of olanzapine and not 20mg. I intend to stay on 5mg indefinitely because it will keep me sane. I have had enough on being on the highest dose possible. I literally do not want to plan anything until this happens.

Although I do have a holiday to America to look forward to, and my plan with that is to buy souvenirs. Even if it's just a simple lighter that I asked for years ago. If I cannot find one in America I will turn to ebay. As you can probably tell, I don't have my priorities right.

I have been on this medication for over 15 years and on the highest dosage possible. So all I want to do is get on to a quarter of that and go from there. We are living through tough times first COVID then the war in Ukraine which has pushed gold prices sky high. I definitely would like to buy more gold and silver with my disposable income as this will not last and is already being eroded away.

A New Hope

by Fatal Whimsy

In a galaxy far far away
Lives a positive me, with hopes and dreams.

In a galaxy far far away
I will have ambitions; realistic ones this time. I will realise my limits. I am not Luke Skywalker, or Princes Lea. I am not on a quest against 'The dark side'. I cannot solve world peace, cure cancer, or "use the force". I am a simple, earthling.

In a galaxy far far away
I won't have to sit in a PIP assessment, AKA "The anti-interview", in which you succeed by not being able to do things. I won't be made to feel the conflicting emotions of humiliation, helplessness, shame and neglect, whilst also feeling like the criminal mastermind of benefit fraud.

In a galaxy far far away
I can keep balance in my life, maintain my health and gain enough wealth for independence. I am not constantly wondering, how the hell I will ever pay back my friends' charitable donations, to the 'I am useless and penniless foundation'.

In a galaxy far far away
I will have a steady income, even on a part time wage. I will have a flexible employer that cares about the impact of stress on my wellbeing and works with me to limit this. I can keep a long term job and stop throwing childish tantrums in the evenings.

In a galaxy far far away
Equality, diversity and disability positive employers will be truly sympathetic to my struggle. They won't just be ticking the boxes on policy forms to keep up appearances.

In a galaxy far far away
My parents can have their well-earned retirement, in peace. My brother and I will no longer be gatecrashing their home, over and over again. I won't have to eat my dad's horrible version of carbonara, which only ever seems to be on the menu, when I'm too depressed to make something else (good god I'm ungrateful).

In a galaxy far far away
Teleportation will be accessible to all, so I won't have to bloody parallel park. Oh wait, that's Star Trek, not Star Wars. Oh well, scrap that then. Let's try this again.

My hope is, "*to seek out new life and new civilizations*".
I'd also quite like "*to boldly go where no one has gone before*"

That, or just buy the winning lottery ticket.

No more

by Ian Watson

Today I breathe, tomorrow?
Strong and Healthy, tomorrow?
Feel of joy of love and tears no more,
Security, comfort, peace of mind, tomorrow?

Stigma, No More
Equality and discrimination, No more
the call of capitalist corruption No More,
A utopian dystopia lay bare, sprawled,
a beating heart, freshly mauled.

Peoples of all banding come together as one
Finding one another, in common goal we unite
The forgotten found anew
The knowledge experience
bequeathed, explored, enriched
The future to come , the fight unknown

Tomorrow is today unfound,
Tomorrow is today anew
Live in the present, live in the now
For the moment called now is all that matters

My hope for the future

by Pauline Hass

I know that all the scientists and doctors are continually doing research to improve all types of medication for all types of diseases, inflections.

I am hoping and wishing that all medical diseases, including HIV, will all just vanish one day. But I suppose that is wishful thinking on my part and will take a huge miracle.

My hope is also to tell my family one day about my HIV status as I have kept it a secret for 10 years now.

My hope is that when my grandchildren are at an age when they can understand diseases and HIV, that they will be open to it and not criticise those who have got a disease or any other medical condition.

If one has hope, then one can improve their quality of life. Have less feelings of hopelessness. Have less stress in their lives. If one has hope, then I think one is more happy, as they have a more positive outlook on life.

Hope is about dreaming and dreaming is a better future for ourselves, especially if one has goals that one wants to attain.

Hope is to wish that the sun will shine after the rain.
Hope is to wish that tomorrow is another day.
Hope is to wish that your grandchildren will grow up to be kind, generous, beautiful adults.

Never give up hope.
Never stop dreaming.

Liz Parkinson

Red lips and red nails

by Liz Parkinson

My thoughts and hopes for the future is freedom, peace.

I long to escape, to be free of the despair.

To spend the rest of my life dancing,

    wearing bright red lipstick and have shiny red nails.

I want to laugh and dance with my sister, to sing out loud.

I want the despair to vanish and leave me alone.

I want to be free.

I want life to be glorious, light and hopeful.

And I want to have bright red lips and shiny red finger nails.

I don't want to be old and invisible.

I want glory, smiles.

I want to be noticed.

First, lose the luggage

by Zoe Robinson

You ask me what my hopes are for the future.

Have you not seen the emotional baggage that surrounds me? My trunk full of trauma, my hat box of shame, my squeaky-wheeled suitcase of despair. I would need to park those somewhere if I were to have any hope for the future. I'd like to find myself a nice husband, maybe I could squeeze him onto my luggage carousel.

I'd like to get my writing published, perhaps my resolve to submit my manuscripts to competitions and agents will stop getting lost down the cracks in the conveyor belt.

I'd like to be more prolific in Mental Health campaigning. I've already spoken at conferences and written reports and participated in university research, but I haven't influenced enough decision-makers. As I said, there's too much baggage in my way.

My focus, right now, is on becoming a good baggage-handler.

Thank you for reading.

A word from our commissioning producer, Charlie Wilkinson

Newcastle University exists to advance education and research and to help society tackle the many challenges it faces. Newcastle University aspires to be a people-focused university that harnesses academic excellence, innovation, and creativity to provide benefits to individuals, to organisations, and to society as a whole.

Newcastle University were keen to work with Mustard Stories Arts CIC and support the next anthology of Words & Worlds around the theme of health and wellbeing. Having people and communities at the centre of our research is something we are passionate about, and the work Mustard Stories Arts do to meaningfully and impactfully engage with communities in the North East is a reflection of our own morals and standards.

We hope this anthology and relationship with Mustard Stories Arts will be an opportunity to support researchers working with people in our region to do so with creative arts and practice at its core; to support our community, as well as our research.

Charlie Wilkinson
Engagement Support Coordinator

Meet the Directors

Mustard Stories Arts is a community interest company based in Tyne and Wear. Our company ethos is all about storytelling for social change; working with communities to provide a platform to tell untold stories through all creative art forms.

"Words and Worlds is the project that led to the creation of this company and it will continue to be our core project. This is the third anthology in the series and we are so excited for there to be more.

It has been a pleasure to facilitate Words and Worlds for the third time. We are incredibly proud of every participant involved and the writers they have become. Thank you for taking the time to read this anthology."

Natasha Haws, Eilis McGowan & Elijah Young

Interns

In this instalment of the Words and Worlds we have had the opportunity to have two interns work with us. These roles are made possible by Newcastle University's Internship programme, it gives them access to relevant and productive experience that they can use in their working lives.

Megan Adams and Isabella Clark were the two working interns on the Words and Worlds project. They both supported the facilitation and delivery of this anthology and had the chance to see a project from start to finish. They were an integral part of the team and we are so pleased they've been a part of Words and Worlds.

Isabella Clark & Megan Adams